Other Titles of Interest

PRACTICAL
ELECTRONIC
SENSORS

by

OWEN BISHOP

BERNARD BABANI (publishing) LTD
THE GRAMPIANS
SHEPHERDS BUSH ROAD
LONDON W6 7NF
ENGLAND

Please Note

Although every care has been taken with the production of this book to ensure that any projects, designs, modifications and/or programs etc. contained herewith, operate in a correct and safe manner and also that all components specified are normally available in Great Britain, the Publishers and Author do not accept responsibility in any way for the failure, including fault in design, of any project, design, modification or program to work correctly or to cause damage to any other equipment that it may be connected to or used in conjunction with, or in respect of any other damage or injury that may be so caused, nor do the Publishers accept responsibility in any way for the failure to obtain specified components.

Notice is also given that if equipment that is still under warranty is modified in any way or used or connected with home-built equipment then that warranty may be void.

© 1991 BERNARD BABANI (publishing) LTD

First Published — September 1991

British Library Cataloguing in Publication Data:
Bishop, O. N. (Owen Neville), *1927–*
    Practical electronic sensors.
    I. Title
    620.0044

    ISBN 0 85934 218 2

Printed and Bound in Great Britain by Cox & Wyman Ltd, Reading

Warning

Certain circuits and projects included in this book involve mains voltages and wiring. These are not recommended for beginners or those with little knowledge or experience of working with mains wiring and voltages.

Introduction

The aim of this book is to describe what electronic sensors are, how they work and how they are used. We have tried to avoid too many technical terms in the descriptions. The few essential terms are explained as we go along.

The sensors are grouped in chapters, so that all the heat sensors appear in one chapter, for example, and all the sound sensors are in another chapter. At the end of each chapter after the first is a practical project. This is to illustrate how to use one of the sensors mentioned in that chapter. The description of how the project works often deals with points about the sensor or the principles of electronic sensing that are not covered in the chapter itself. Even if you do not intend to build the project, it is worthwhile reading 'How it works' in the project description. A few of the chapters have a second project using a different sensor.

The projects are chosen so that they will be of interest to the hobbyist and have applications in and around the home. There is no attempt to produce devices suitable for critical use in industrial applications, but many of the circuits may be helpful for students who have to design and build a project as part of an examination. To help readers to select a suitable project, they are graded according to difficulty:

      1 — suitable for beginners
      2 — for the average constructor
      3 — for advanced constructors

The project descriptions include a circuit diagram, an account of how the project works, advice on construction, and details of components, where these are not obvious from the circuit diagram. Pin numbers of ICs are given in the diagrams, except for ICs containing several identical gates. With these, it does not matter which particular gate is used for a given part of the circuit. Much depends on the way the components are laid out on the constructor's PCB or stripboard, connections to particular gates being made with the idea of simplifying the wiring or PCB pattern. Refer to the appendix for pin-outs of these ICs, where you will also find pin-outs of transistors and similar components. Resistor values are specified in the circuit diagrams. Unless otherwise instructed, use 5% tolerance resistors, either the ¼W carbon film type or (better) the 0.6W metal film type.

Contents

Chapter 1

SENSORS AND SENSING

A sensor is a device that is used to detect a physical quantity. We have sensors that detect light, or sound, or mechanical force, or a magnetic field, or various other physical quantities. The Bourdon tube (Fig. 1.1) is an example of a sensor, which is used to sense gas pressure. Operating on the same principle as the blow-out toy often found in Christmas crackers, the tube becomes straighter as the gas pressure inside it increases relative to the gas pressure outside. When the pressure inside decreases, the curvature of the tube increases.

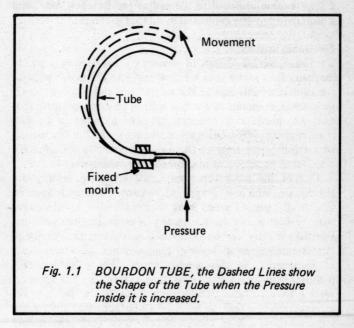

Fig. 1.1   BOURDON TUBE, the Dashed Lines show the Shape of the Tube when the Pressure inside it is increased.

The Bourdon tube has all the essential features of a sensor:
  * it is affected by the physical quantity it is designed to sense, but little affected by other physical quantities (for

example, temperature, humidity, or vibration);

* any change in the physical quantity produces a change in the sensor, in this example, a change in its shape;

* the amount of change in the sensor is related to the amount of change in the physical quantity; the bigger the pressure difference, the more the tube uncurls;

* a very small change in pressure may not cause a perceptible change of shape — there are limits on the *sensitivity* of the sensor;

* a very large change in pressure may permanently distort or even destroy the sensor — there are limits on the *operating range* of the sensor;

* although it may be possible to use the sensor on its own, it is more useful if it is connected to an *amplifier* (for example, a lever system attached to the end of the Bourdon tube) and a *display* (e.g. a dial graduated in units of pressure).

Electronic Sensors

We began our discussion of sensors by considering a purely mechanical example, but we now move to *electronic* sensors, the subject of this book. The function of electronic sensors is to convert a change in a non-electrical physical quantity (for example, pressure or temperature) into a change in an electrical quantity (for example, resistance). In the discussions which follow we refer to the non-electrical physical quantity which is to be sensed or measured as the *measurand*.

One of the most commonly used electronic sensors is a *thermistor*, which is a type of resistor. The resistance of almost all resistors varies with temperature so, by measuring their resistance, we have a means of measuring temperature. For the ordinary carbon or metal-film resistors that we use in circuit-building, an increase of temperature causes an increase of resistance, but this is only small. For a high-stability resistor the increase may be as little as 0.025% of the resistor value for every degree Celsius rise in temperature. By contrast, a thermistor is a resistor made of a substance specially formulated to show a large change of resistance when temperature changes. As explained on page 41, where we describe the thermistors in more detail, the substance is moulded into a bar, a disc or a bead with two terminal wires attached (Fig. 1.2).

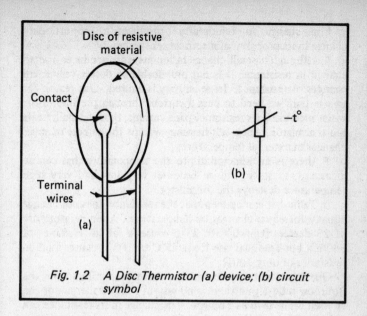

Fig. 1.2   A Disc Thermistor (a) device; (b) circuit
symbol

In contrast to ordinary resistors, most thermistors show a
decrease in resistance as temperature increases. We say that
they have a *negative temperature coefficient* (NTC). The
resistance of a typical NTC thermistor decreases with temperature as shown in Table 1.

Table 1

Temperature (°C)	Resistance (Ω)
0	5300
25	1500
50	500
75	200
100	100

A thermistor has many of the properties of a typical sensor,
as listed earlier:

* it is strongly affected by temperature, but not by other
physical quantities such as light, pressure or humidity;

* a change in temperature produces a proportionate change in its property of electrical resistance;

* although a small change in temperature produces a small change in resistance, it is not practicable to detect very small changes of resistance. Its sensitivity is limited. One reason for this is that we need to pass a current through the thermistor when measuring its resistance; this current, though small, heats the thermistor. Such self-heating swamps the effects of small changes in external temperature;

* there is an upper limit to the temperature that can be measured, as its resistance becomes very low and very high temperature destroys the thermistor.

In Table 1 it can be seen that the resistance does not change equally for equal changes of temperature. A temperature rise of 25 degrees from 0°C to 25°C causes a fall in resistance of 3800Ω, but an equal rise from 75°C to 100°C causes a fall in resistance of only 100Ω.

One important way in which a thermistor differs from the Bourdon tube is that there is no way in which a thermistor can be used on its own as a sensor. The change in its resistance can only be detected electrically. The least we need is a circuit to pass a current through it and meters to measure this current and the voltage across the thermistor. From these two readings we calculate the resistance in ohms, and from this we can calculate the temperature. In practice a more elaborate circuit would be used, which would calculate the temperature for us and display the temperature in degrees. In technical terms, we need *electronic processing* of the output of the sensor to give us a direct reading of the measurand on some kind of *display* device. Ways of doing this are described later in this section. Before reaching that section, there are some terms and ideas that need to be discussed.

Linearity
Ideally the output of a sensor should change equally for equal changes in the measurand. The response of such a sensor is described as being *linear*. If we plot a graph relating the measurand to the response of a linear sensor, we obtain a straight line. This is far from what we find with the thermistor featured in Table 1. Fortunately, there are many other

4

sensors which have a perfectly linear response. We mention several examples of these in later chapters.

A linear response is often advantageous, for it simplifies the design of the processing circuit which converts this response into a reading on a display. But, for the sake of convenience, cost, robustness or some other advantageous feature, we may sometimes prefer to use a non-linear sensor and correct for its non-linearity in the processing stage before displaying the result. The simplest way of correcting is to mark the display dial with a non-linear scale, but there are also electronic ways of making the corrections.

There is one application of sensors in which linearity is usually unimportant. This is when the sensor is required to detect when the measurand reaches one particular level. For example, if a thermistor is being used as the sensor in a fire alarm, the system can be set to sound the alarm when the resistance of the thermistor reaches a certain value. Its resistance at temperatures lower or higher than the set point is immaterial, and so its lack of linearity is no disadvantage.

Measurement and Control

These are the two main fields in which sensors are used. Some sensors are used mainly in one field or the other but the thermistor has applications in both. In the field of measurement we use thermistors in electronic thermometers with a dial or numeric display, that indicates temperature. With a little more sophistication, the electronic thermometer can be made to register and display the minimum and maximum temperatures reached since it was last reset. In the field of control, a thermistor can be used in a thermostat system to maintain a constant temperature in a room, refrigerator, or incubator. In this application it needs to have no display to show what the room temperature is; its essential function is to control it at a constant level. Another control application is the fire alarm, which turns on the siren when the temperature exceeds a given level. The topics of measurement and control are discussed in more detail in Chapters 13 and 14.

Sensors and Transducers

The term *transducer* is sometimes used loosely as if it means the same as *sensor*, but there are entirely different concepts behind these two words. We have already defined a sensor as a device that responds to a change in the measurand by a change in one of its physical properties. In the case of electronic sensors, the physical property changed is electrical. The thermistor is a good example of this, as a change in temperature (the measurand) causes a change in one of its electrical properties (resistance).

A transducer is defined as a device which converts one form of energy to another form of energy. Its essential function is *energy conversion.* Thus a thermistor is not a transducer because there is no energy conversion, and its resistance is not a form of energy. Conversely, an electric motor is a transducer because it converts electrical energy into mechanical energy, but it is not a sensor.

There are some devices which are both sensors and transducers, and perhaps it is because of these that the confusion has arisen. For example, the crystal in a microphone converts the energy of sound waves to electrical energy (p. 102), so it is a transducer. We make use of this transducing property for sensing sounds, so it also ranks as a sensor. Even in this example, it could be considered that, when the crystal is used in a microphone, the amount of energy transduced is too small to warrant calling the crystal a transducer. The crystal in a trigger-operated gas-lighter, in which a relatively large amount of energy from the operator's finger is converted into a high-voltage electrical spark, is a better instance of transduction.

Electromotive Force and Related Terms
Electromotive force (or e.m.f.) is an electrical force produced by the action of a transducer. It is a force which, given the chance, will cause a current to flow around a circuit. A dry cell or 'battery' is a common example of a transducing device which produces e.m.f. The e.m.f. is the result of the conversion of chemical energy into electrical energy in the cell. This force exists whether or not there is a circuit connected to the cell and a current is actually flowing from the cell. E.m.f. is expressed in *volts.*

The result of e.m.f. is a *potential difference* (p.d.) between the terminals of the cell. Again, if there is an electrical connection, a current flows from a point at high (positive) potential to a point at low (negative) potential. The greater the p.d., the larger the current. P.d. too is expressed in volts. In practice, we often loosely refer to both e.m.f. and p.d. as voltage.

If a dry cell is not connected into a circuit, no current flows and the p.d. has the same value as the e.m.f. When the cell is connected to a circuit, current flows, and has to pass not only through the wires and components of the circuit but also through the materials of the cell. These materials offer electrical resistance to the flow of current, known as the *internal resistance* of the cell. This does not affect the e.m.f. which is constant as long as the cell is fresh. But always when a current flows through a resistance there is a drop of voltage across the resistance. This is simply a consequence of Ohm's Law, and the three quantities are related by the familiar equation, $V = IR$. The internal resistance of a cell is usually low, so the voltage drop is small, but nevertheless there is a drop. Figure 1.3 shows what happens. The effect of internal resistance is to make the p.d. across the terminals of the cell less than its e.m.f. The amount of drop depends on the amount of current being drawn. This is why a 'flat' car battery may have a p.d. great enough to light the dashboard lamps, but this falls dramatically when the starter motor draws a heavy current.

A similar situation arises with sensors that produce an e.m.f. by transducing forms of energy such as light, heat or sound. The p.d. across the terminals of the sensor falls if too large a current is being drawn from them. This may give rise to serious errors of measurement. We design processing circuits to take as little current as possible from the sensor.

Electronic Sensing
The most frequently used electrical properties of electronic sensors are:

* resistance
* capacitance
* inductance
* production of an electromotive force (e.m.f.).

7

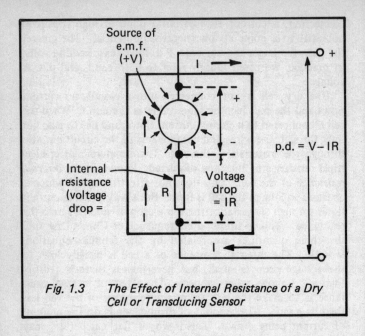

Fig. 1.3   *The Effect of Internal Resistance of a Dry Cell or Transducing Sensor*

Although a wide variety of sensors exists, responding to many different measurands, the fact that only four electrical quantities are commonly involved means that most processing circuits are versions of a few basic designs, depending on which quantity is to be processed:

1 Processing changes in e.m.f.

Quartz and several other crystalline materials generate an e.m.f. when they are subjected to mechanical strain. This is known as the *piezo-electric effect*. When pressure is exerted on such a crystal so as to distort its shape, an e.m.f. often up to several kilovolts is generated between opposite faces of the crystal. It has already been mentioned that this property is used to produce the spark in trigger-operated gas-lighters. The piezo-electric effect is widely used in sensors such as crystal microphones and other devices in which changes in pressure or force are to be converted to changes in e.m.f.

8

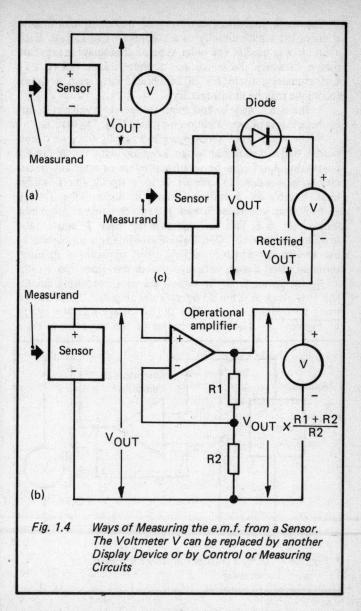

Fig. 1.4   Ways of Measuring the e.m.f. from a Sensor.
The Voltmeter V can be replaced by another
Display Device or by Control or Measuring
Circuits

The most straightforward way of measuring e.m.f. is to connect the sensor directly to a voltmeter (Fig. 1.4(a)). Such a circuit was used in the older type of photographic exposure meter, in which the sensor was a photo-voltaic cell (p. 21). Unfortunately, there are often reasons why such a simple technique may be unsatisfactory.

* the e.m.f. may be too small to operate a voltmeter; one or more stages of amplification may help (Fig. 1.4(b));
* the e.m.f. may be changing too rapidly for a voltmeter needle, or a digital display to keep up with it. A rapidly alternating e.m.f. can be rectified, before or after any necessary amplification, to convert it to a steady (d.c.) voltage level, suitable for operating a meter or display (Fig. 1.4(c));
* if the voltmeter draws too much current from the sensor, the p.d. falls, as explained on page 7, and a false reading is obtained. One way of avoiding this problem is to use a voltmeter which has a field-effect transistor at its input terminal; this draws virtually no current from the sensor.

If the sensor is to be connected to a processing circuit, the first stage is often an operational amplifier. One way of using an operational amplifier is the *voltage follower* circuit of Figure 1.5. The input terminal of the amplifier offers a

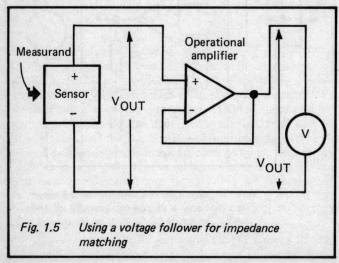

Fig. 1.5   Using a voltage follower for impedance matching

resistance of several megohms. Consequently only a minute current is drawn from the sensor. The amplifier has a gain of 1, so the output of the amplifier is exactly equal to that of the sensor. It may seem that there is no point in using this circuit. The advantage is that, unlike the sensor, the amplifier can supply a large current to subsequent stages, without any significant drop in its output voltage. The amplifier output supplies enough current and to spare, to drive an ordinary voltmeter or a wide range of processing circuits. The circuit of Figure 1.4(b) is similar in that the amplifier draws virtually no current from the sensor and can itself supply a large current, but it also amplifies the voltage produced by the sensor. The amount of amplification depends on the values selected for the resistors.

2 Processing changes in resistance

The simplest technique for detecting the changes in resistance of a sensor is to make the sensor part of a potential divider circuit, as in Figure 1.6. If the supply voltage is V_{IN}, the p.d. across the series resistor R is given by:

$$V_{OUT} = V_{IN} \frac{R}{R + R_s}$$

The final step is to measure V_{OUT}, using one of the techniques described in section 1 above. One of the main disadvantages of the potential divider method is that it relies on the sensor and series resistor having relatively high resistances, so that a reasonably small current generates an appreciable p.d. With a low-resistance sensor, such as a platinum thermometer (page 43), the current is large and heats the sensor, giving rise to errors. Another disadvantage is that the method does not readily detect small variations in a relatively large resistance; it lacks sensitivity. Finally, for resistive sensors such as strain gauges (page 61) that are affected also by temperature, the circuit offers no means of temperature compensation.

A number of circuits based on the Wheatstone Bridge are used for more precise processing of resistance changes. The principle of the bridge is illustrated in Figure 1.7. The bridge

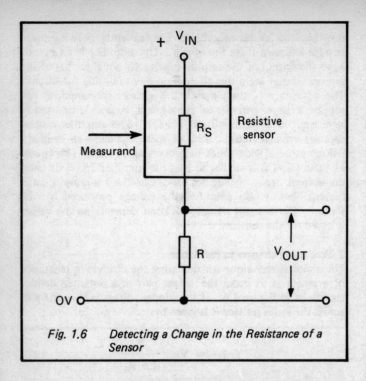

Fig. 1.6   Detecting a Change in the Resistance of a Sensor

consists of four branches or *arms*, each containing a resistance. A p.d. V_{IN} is applied across the bridge at points A and C, causing currents to flow along the routes ABC and ADC. The p.d. V_{OUT} between points B and D is measured by a voltmeter or voltage-sensitive circuit. If the ratio R1/R2 is equal to the ratio R3/R4 the potential at B equals that at D, so V_{OUT} is zero. The bridge is said to be *balanced*. One particular situation in which the bridge balances is when all four resistors are exactly equal. If any one of the resistances increases or decreases slightly, the bridge is thrown out of balance. For example, if the resistor in arm AB increases in value the potential at B falls, but there is no change in the potential at D. This creates a p.d. between B and D. It requires only a relatively small change in one of the resistances to produce an appreciable change in p.d. A circuit connected to B and D is used to

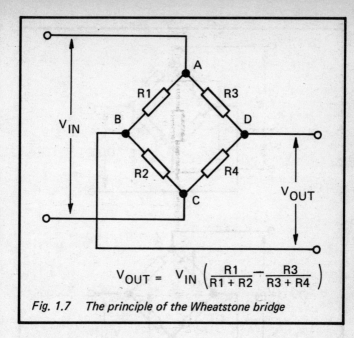

$$V_{OUT} = V_{IN} \left(\frac{R1}{R1 + R2} - \frac{R3}{R3 + R4} \right)$$

Fig. 1.7   The principle of the Wheatstone bridge

measure the p.d. and perhaps to amplify it, in the same way as described in section 1 above.

Various versions of the bridge circuit are illustrated in Figure 1.8. The quarter bridge includes the sensor in one arm, represented by the variable resistor symbol. A trimmer resistor is often connected in this arm, in series with the sensor, and is used when balancing the bridge to set the zero point. The half bridge is more sensitive, incorporating two sensors in arms AB and CD so that their changes of resistance act in the opposite direction. An increase in the resistance of the sensors lowers the potential at B and raises it at D. Thus, compared with the quarter bridge, the half bridge gives double the change in output for a given change in the measurand. The full bridge includes a sensor in each arm, the sensors being arranged so that two respond in the opposite way to the other two, as indicated by the directions of the arrows. This gives even greater output, but is applicable only to certain types of

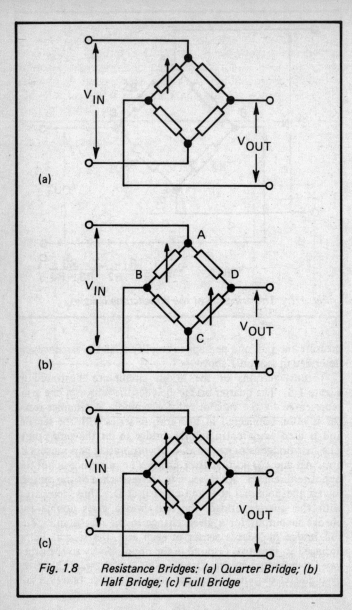

Fig. 1.8   Resistance Bridges: (a) Quarter Bridge; (b) Half Bridge; (c) Full Bridge

sensor, such as strain gauges (page 63).

One feature of a bridge is that it can be wired so as to compensate automatically for certain errors. Effects of temperature on lead resistance can be compensated for by wiring a dummy lead into the bridge, as in Figure 1.9. Changes in lead resistance are equal in both arms so the ratio R1/R2

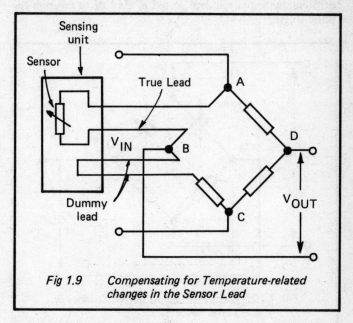

Fig 1.9   *Compensating for Temperature-related changes in the Sensor Lead*

remains unaltered and the balance of the bridge is unaffected. In the bolometer described on page 48, the sensing thermistor is in arm AB and there is an identical second thermistor in arm BD. The second thermistor is shielded from the radiation falling on the sensor, so the potential at B varies with radiation intensity. On the other hand both thermistors are equally affected by changes in ambient temperature, the temperature inside the case of the bolometer. Changes in the resistance of both thermistors due to this have no effect on the ratio R1/R2 and consequently the potential at B remains unaffected by changes in ambient temperature.

3 Processing changes in capacitance

One way of doing this is to use the capacitative sensor as the timing capacitor in an oscillator or pulse-generating circuit. In this way changes in capacitance are converted to changes in the frequency of the oscillator, or in the length of the pulse. Often a digital circuit is used either for counting the number of oscillations in a standard period of time or to measure the pulse length.

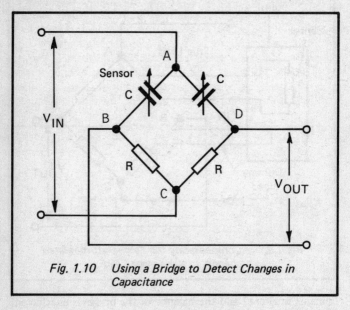

Fig. 1.10   Using a Bridge to Detect Changes in Capacitance

The bridge circuit can also be adapted for capacitative sensors (Fig. 1.10). An alternating voltage is applied to the bridge, and the impedance of the sensor and the variable capacitor act in a similar way to the resistors of the ordinary bridge. The variable capacitor C is adjusted to bring the bridge into balance, with zero output, at the zero point of the measurand. If the value of the measurand changes, the capacitance of the sensor changes, putting the bridge out of balance and causing an alternating p.d. to appear at the output. Bridge detection is particularly useful if the sensor has two capacitative outputs, which act in opposite directions. These capacitances are used in two arms of the bridge AB and AD, giving a greater output than for a single capacitance.

4 Processing changes in inductance

The techniques available are similar to those used for capacitance. The inductive sensor may be made part of an oscillator, so that variations in its inductance appear as variations in the frequency of the oscillator. Bridge methods are also used.

A related technique depends on variations in the electromagnetic linking (or magnetic resistance, or *reluctance*) between two or more coils. A popular example of this technique is a *linear variable differential transformer*, known as an LVDT for short. The LVDT is the basis of many types of sensor in which position is the measurand. Fig. 1.11 illustrates the principle and examples of its use appear in Chapter 5.

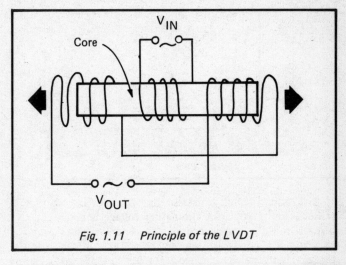

Fig. 1.11   Principle of the LVDT

An alternating current is passed through a coil, generating a magnetic field which is linked by means of a ferromagnetic core to two coils wired in series with each other. When the core is in its central position, the e.m.f.s induced in the two coils are equal and opposite so the output of the LVDT is

17

zero. If the core is displaced one way or the other the linkage between the central coil and one outer coil becomes stronger, but that between the central coil and the other outer coil becomes weaker. Consequently the e.m.f. generated in the coils are unequal and no longer cancel out. The amplitude of the alternating output signal increases by an amount depending on the displacement of the core. The position of any object that is mechanically linked to the core can thus be sensed.

Chapter 2

RADIATION SENSORS

One essential attribute of radiation is that it originates in one place and travels to another. For this reason, radiation sensors are often concerned with sensing and measuring at a distance. Distances may be very great, as when we use a spectrometer to analyse the light emitted by a distant star and to tell us about the chemical composition of the star. The distance is much less when we use light to read the bar code on a packet of corn flakes at the supermarket check-out.

When we speak of radiation we mean one of the kinds of *electromagnetic radiation*. Electromagnetic radiation consists of an electrical field and a magnetic field, oscillating at right angles to each other and to the direction in which the electromagnetic radiation is travelling. The nature of the radiation depends on its wavelength. Radio waves have the longest wavelengths, up to several kilometres long. There are no sensors for radio waves, no devices that respond when radio waves are present. We detect waves by radio-frequency resonant circuits in radio receivers. Shorter in wavelength than radio waves are microwaves, which are detectable by microwave (or radar) receivers. Radio and microwave receivers are both outside the scope of this book.

With decreasing wavelength we next come to infra-red radiation (IR) then the visible radiation that we call *light*, and then ultra-violet radiation (UV). Their wavelength ranges from about 1mm for the longest IR down to 1nm for the shortest UV. The human body has sensors for IR, which we detect by the heat produced when IR falls on the skin. Our eyes are light sensors, but we have no means of sensing UV, except by its effect in producing a suntan or, in excess, causing skin cancer. It is with IR, light and UV that the sensors in this chapter are concerned.

Shorter than UV are the wavelengths of X-rays and gamma rays, also damaging to the human body in excess. Gamma rays have the shortest wavelength of all known electromagnetic radiation, as little as 10^{-13} m. Gamma rays reach the

Earth from outer space, and are known as cosmic radiation. More important sources of gamma rays are the radioactive substances used in nuclear power and in many industrial applications. Nuclear radiation includes not only the electromagnetic gamma radiation, but also several types of sub-atomic particles. These particles and the devices sensitive to them are described in Chapter 9.

Although we have described electromagnetic radiation as if it consists of waves, it has also been proved that it has some of the properties of particles. It may be difficult to understand how this can be so, but this is only because such an idea is so far beyond the range of experiences of everyday life. A particle of radiation is called a *photon*. Each photon possesses a certain amount of energy; the shorter the wavelength the greater the energy of the photon. This is why UV, X-rays and gamma rays do so much damage when they strike the human body. However, it is this energy which is responsible for what happens in IR, light and UV sensors. The photons falling on the sensitive material of the sensor possess sufficient energy to displace electrons from the material. In some sensors, the electrons are knocked right out of the material. In others they are freed from the atoms with which they were associated to become charge carriers in the material. We describe the effects in more detail later.

When selecting a radiation sensor for a particular purpose there are a number of points that need to be considered:

* *responsitivity* – the output of the sensor at a given level of illumination. For visible light, the level of illumination may be expressed in lux, 50 lux being the level of normal domestic lighting; direct sunlight is in the order of 100,000 lux. More often, for IR, light and UV, the sensitivity is related to the energy received by the sensor, usually expressed in milliwatts per square centimetre. The way the corresponding output is expressed depends upon the nature of the sensor;

* *peak sensitivity* – the wavelength at which the sensor shows maximum response. Response peaks often occur at the extremes of the visible spectrum, at the IR, red or blue wavelengths. In such cases it may be necessary to use light filters to match the response characteristics to those required in the application;

* *response time* — different types of radiation sensor vary considerably in this respect. If the measurand is changing rapidly, particularly if it is alternating at high frequency, it is essential to use a sensor which has a short response time.

The main types of radiation sensor are as follows:

1 Photovoltaic cell

A photovoltaic cell is a device which converts the energy of incident radiation into electrical energy. It is a transducer, producing an e.m.f. when it is illuminated. The size of the e.m.f. depends linearly on the intensity of the radiation, so photovoltaic cells make excellent sensors.

The original photovoltaic cell was the selenium cell, consisting of an iron plate coated with a layer of selenium. Nowadays the silicon semiconductors are used. Figure 2.1 shows a section through a *p on n* semiconductor photovoltaic cell. The silicon is doped to convert it to n-type material except for the very thin upper layer, which is p-type. This layer is almost transparent and allows light to penetrate. As in the ordinary silicon diode, which also consists of a junction between p-type and n-type silicon, a *depletion layer* automatically forms on either side of the pn junction. Electrons drift across the junction from the n-type layer, leaving some of the atoms on that side as positive ions. Conversely, holes (vacancies where electrons are 'missing' from an atom, and therefore equivalent to a positive charge) drift across from the p-type layer leaving negative ions on that side. Thus there are fixed ions but no mobile charge carriers in the depletion layer. The regions of negative and positive ions constitute a *virtual cell* across the junction. Its e.m.f. is about 0.7V, with the n-type positive of the p-type layer. In this respect the structure and behaviour of the photovoltaic cell is the same as that of any silicon diode, including the photodiode (see later).

When radiation falls on the pn junction of the photovoltaic cell, the arriving photons excite the electrons of the semiconductor to escape from the atoms of the semiconductor, leaving vacancies (holes) in the crystal structure. The electric field at the pn junction (the virtual cell) attracts the electrons to the n-type material and the holes to the p-type material. If the cell is connected into a circuit, the excess electrons in the

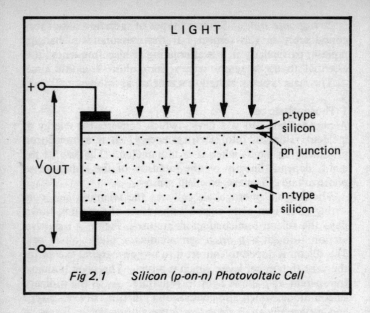

Fig 2.1   Silicon (p-on-n) Photovoltaic Cell

n-type flow through the circuit to combine with the excess holes in the p-type. As long as radiation falls on the cell, the supply of electrons and holes is continually renewed, generating an e.m.f., with the p-type positive of the n-type. Thus the photovoltaic cell produces its own e.m.f. and does not need any external power supply.

Photovoltaic cells are typically manufactured with a large area, to enhance their sensitivity. One such device has an area of 100mm², and a responsivity of 0.5A per watt of radiant energy received. Response is linear and the response time is in the order of 50ns. The peak sensitivity of these devices is usually at about 800–900nm, in the red/IR part of the spectrum.

The applications of photovoltaic cells include optical instruments and communication by optical means, including fibre-optics. Their linear response is valuable in the first type of application and their rapid response time is essential for the second. Some, such as the BPW21, have a colour filter incorporated in the window of the device, giving a peak of sensitivity at about 550nm, in the yellow region of the spectrum. Because its overall sensitivity approximates to that of the human eye, it is specially useful for colour-matching. Solar cells have a similar construction and action. They are used as transducers for power generation in remote areas, spacecraft and satellites.

2 Photodiode

The photodiode has similar structure and action to the photovoltaic cell, indeed some devices can be used in either mode. The sensitive surface is smaller in a photodiode, many photodiodes being simply ordinary diodes enclosed in a clear glass capsule instead of opaque ones. A photodiode requires an external power supply, and is connected so that it is reverse-biassed (Fig. 2.2). The diode is unable to conduct using its *majority carriers* (electrons in n-type and holes in p-type) that have been deliberately introduced into the semiconductor. These are unable to cross the depletion layer. However, there is always a relatively small number of *minority carriers* present, holes in the n-type and electrons in the p-type.

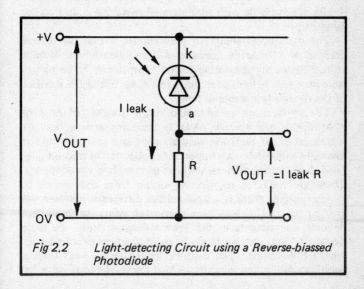

Fig 2.2   *Light-detecting Circuit using a Reverse-biassed Photodiode*

These are produced when atoms in the semiconductor are excited by thermal action (random movements of the atoms related to temperature). As a result a very small reverse or leakage current (a few nanoamps) is able to pass through the diode. When the pn junction is exposed to light, energy is absorbed by the atoms increasing their thermal energy and releasing additional carriers. The reverse current increases. If the current is passed through a high-value resistor, a measurable p.d. is generated across it, which can be measured by various means (page 9).

The peak sensitivity of most photodiodes is toward the red end of the spectrum and some types are specifically designed as infra-red photodiodes. The response is linear and the response time is fast, typically 250ns. PIN photodiodes have a layer of pure (intrinsic) semiconductor sandwiched between the p-type and n-type layers. The effect of increasing the gap between the p-type and n-type layers is to decrease the capacitance of the device. As a result, it is able to follow rapid changes in light level more rapidly. Thus these devices have a very rapid response time. For example, the BPX65 has a response time of only 0.5ns. For switching purposes, photodiodes are available with an integrated switching circuit on the same chip.

The main disadvantage of photodiodes is that the reverse current is necessarily small and consequently the output voltage from the measuring circuit is small too. The phototransistor (see below) overcomes this snag, but at the sacrifice of the diode's fast response time.

The applications of photodiodes are similar to those of photovoltaic cells though, owing to their smaller area, they are less suitable for precision measurement and for operation at low light intensities. An important application of photodiodes (and also phototransistors, see next section) is in optocouplers. These are used for transferring signals from one circuit to another where there is a large voltage difference between the two circuits. This may be a matter of safety or to protect delicate components in the lower-voltage circuit. In these devices a light-emitting diode is sealed in a light-proof package with a photodiode. The electrical insulation between them is proof against potential differences of several thousand volts.

Variations in the input signal causes variations in the amount of light emitted by the LED. The photodiode is sensitive to this light and a corresponding signal appears across it.

3 Phototransistor

This is a transistor enclosed in a can with a transparent lens, so that light can reach the base layer (Fig. 2.3). The base is

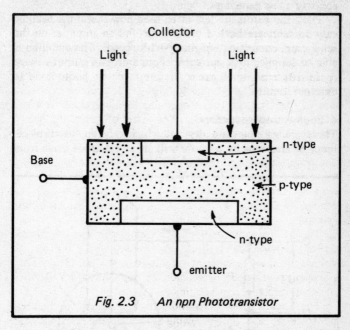

Fig. 2.3   An npn Phototransistor

not normally connected to the external circuit. Incident light causes the production of electron-hole pairs at the reverse-biassed collector-base junction, just as it does in a photodiode.

The effect is the same as if there is a small current flowing from base to emitter. With a p.d. applied between collector and emitter, the transistor action of the base-emitter current, causes a much larger current to flow from collector to emitter. In short, we can consider the phototransistor as a photodiode with built-in amplification. Although the phototransistor has greater sensitivity than the photodiode, it is also much slower in action. Response times are rated in milliseconds rather than in nanoseconds. Peak sensitivity is in the same region as for photodiodes.

The sensitivity of the phototransistor may be increased by incorporating a second transistor on the same chip, the two being connected as a Darlington pair. Currents of several milliamps are produced in the light, but currents in the dark are only a few nanoamps.

Phototransistors are less often used now that it has become easy to fabricate both a photodiode and an amplifier on the same chip, combining sensitivity with speed. The amplifier is able to supply a large current without a drop in output voltage (page 10), making it easier to interface the photodiode to external circuits.

4 Photoemissive detectors
These are gaseous-state devices, which rely on the displacement of electrons by photons striking an electrode made from

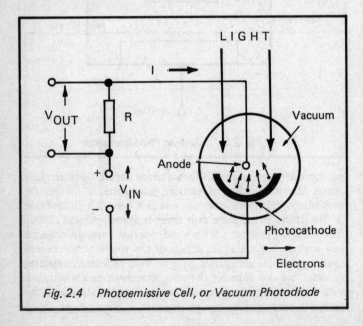

Fig. 2.4   Photoemissive Cell, or Vacuum Photodiode

a sensitive metal or alloy. The simplest form is a vacuum photodiode (Fig. 2.4). An external p.d. is applied between the sensitive photocathode and the anode. Under illumination, electrons are displaced from the atoms of the photocathode cathode and accelerated across to the anode. The flow of electrons is equivalent to a conventional current flowing from anode to the photocathode. This current is passed through a resistor, causing a p.d. V_{OUT} to be generated. This p.d. is measured by one of the standard techniques (page 10).

The *photomultiplier tube* is an extension of the principle of the vacuum photodiode. The tube has a number of electrodes in addition to the photocathode and anode (Fig. 2.5). These electrodes, known as *dynodes* are connected to a resistor network so that there is an increasing potential from the photocathode, along the array of dynodes, to the anode. Incident light photons displace electrons from the photocathode as in the vacuum photodiode. These electrons are

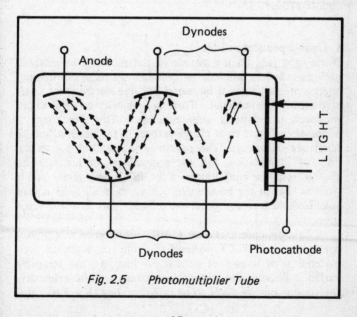

Fig. 2.5   Photomultiplier Tube

accelerated by the electric field between the photocathode and the first dynode. The acceleration gives them greater energy so that, when they reach the dynode, each electron is able to displace several electrons from it. The increased number of electrons is then accelerated toward the second dynode. The burst of electrons passes from dynode to dynode increasing in numbers at each stage until it eventually reaches the anode. The effect is an amplification of the current by a factor of several million, depending on the number of dynodes in the tube.

Photomultipliers are extremely sensitive and have response times of only 10ns. Depending on the materials used for the photocathode, they can be sensitised to different regions of the spectrum, including ultra-violet. They require a well-regulated high-voltage power supply, in the region of 1000V. Photomultipliers can detect the arrival of a single photon, and are usable only under the lowest illumination levels. In astronomy they measure the light from distant stars. They have several other scientific applications, including scintillation counters (page 136).

5 Light-dependent resistor

When light falls on the surface of a semiconductor material such as cadmium sulphide or cadmium selenide, the thermal energy of the atoms is increased and free electrons are liberated within the material. These are minority carriers, so are produced in relatively large numbers. This effect greatly increases the number of charge carriers in the material and its resistance decreases. The resistance varies according to the level of illumination, but the response is not linear. The spectral response covers most of the visible light region and is close to that of the human eye. Other materials such as lead sulphide and mercury cadmium telluride also have the same property.

A light-dependent resistor (LDR), also known as a *photo-conductive cell* (PCC), consists of a disc or block of such material with a pair of conductors fused to the receptive surface. Because the material has a high specific resistivity, the conductors are made to be interdigitating (Fig. 2.6). This

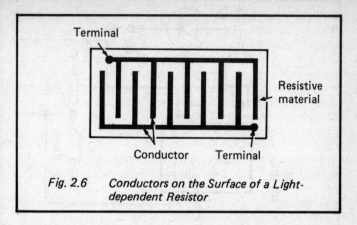

Fig. 2.6   *Conductors on the Surface of a Light-dependent Resistor*

gives a wide but very short conducting path across the surface of the material.

LDRs have the advantages that they are inexpensive and easy to use. Sensitivity is high, the resistance of a typical LDR, the ORP12, falling from $10M\Omega$ in darkness to $2.4k\Omega$ at 50 lux and to 130Ω at 1000 lux. Their main disadvantage is their slow response-time. The turn-on time is about 350ms; this is the time taken for the resistance to fall when the device is illuminated. The turn-off time is about 75ms. Note that these times are expressed in *milli*seconds, compared with times in nanoseconds for most other light sensors.

6 Pyroelectric sensor and pyrometers

These IR sensors are used for detecting changes of temperature or measuring temperature at a distance. They are described in Chapter 3, which deals with temperature sensors.

PROJECT 1 – Sunshine Duration Meter (Level 3)

This device measures the number of hours of sunshine received daily. It makes an interesting addition to the home weather station.

How It Works

There are two sensors in this project, the identical light-dependent resistors R3 and R4 (Fig. 2.7), mounted side-by-

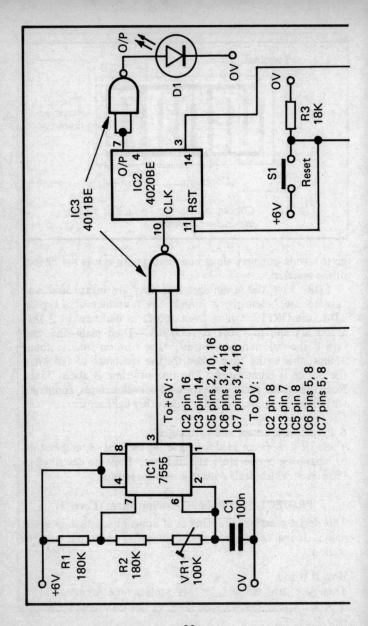

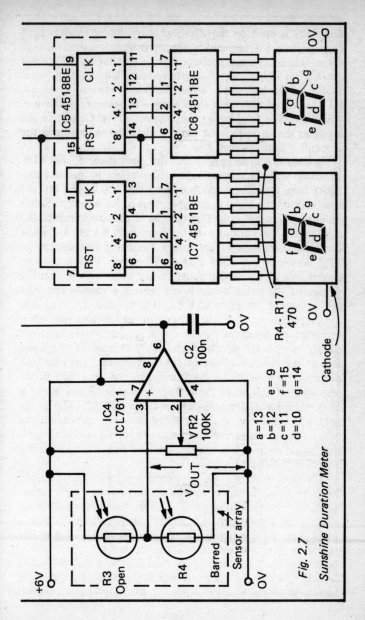

Fig. 2.7

Sunshine Duration Meter

IC5 4518BE

IC6 4511BE

IC7 4511BE

IC4 ICL7611

C2 100n

VR2 100K

R4 - R17 470

Cathode

Sensor array

R3 Open

R4 Barred

+6V

0V

V_OUT

a=13
b=12
c=11
d=10
e=9
f=15
g=14

side. R3 is open to the whole sky, so that it receives light directly from the Sun and indirectly from the rest of the sky. R4 is shielded from the direct rays of the Sun by an opaque curving bar (Fig. 2.8), so it receives only indirect light, from clouds or the blue sky. When the Sun is covered by cloud, R4 receives slightly less light than R3 because of the bar. When the Sun is shining, the amount of light reaching R3 increases dramatically, but there is virtually no change in the amount of light reaching R4.

As explained on page 28, the resistance of an LDR decreases with increasing light. The effect is that the two LDRs have a similar resistance in cloudy conditions, but the resistance of R3 is much less than that of R4 when the Sun is shining. A bridge circuit (page 13) is used to compare the resistances. Two arms of the bridge contain R3 and R4, while the other two arms of the bridge consist of the sections of VR2 which lie on either side of its wiper. VR2 is used to *almost* balance the bridge under cloudy conditions, so that the voltage at the point between the sensors is slightly less than the voltage at the wiper of VR2. The voltages are compared by the amplifier IC4, the output of which goes low (0V). Increases or decreases in cloudiness or in the thickness of clouds have almost equal effects on the resistances of R3 and R4, so the balance of the bridge is unaltered. The amplifier output stays low. When the Sun shines, the large drop in the resistance of R3 raises the voltage between R3 and R4 to a level much higher than that at the wiper of VR2. The bridge goes out of balance, in the opposite direction, and the output of the amplifier rises to 6V. C2 serves to damp out oscillations that might occur when the amplifier output is changing from one state to the other.

The action of the sensor circuit results in a low output from the amplifier under cloudy conditions and a high output when the Sun is shining. This is a logical output that can be used in the timing circuit. The timing circuit is based on a 'clock', an astable multivibrator running at 27.3Hz. The period is determined by R1, R2, VR1 and C1. Only a low-value capacitor is needed, so this can be a polycarbonate capacitor, which is stable enough for accurate timing. The output from the timer and the amplifier are fed to a NAND

32

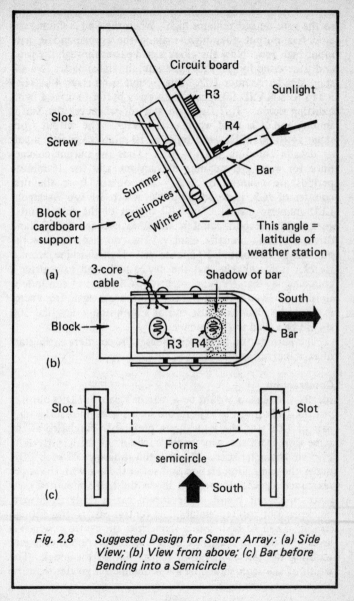

Fig. 2.8   Suggested Design for Sensor Array: (a) Side View; (b) View from above; (c) Bar before Bending into a Semicircle

gate. Under cloudy conditions the amplifier output is low, so the gate output remains high. When the Sun is shining the amplifier output goes high, making the corresponding gate input high too. Now the clock signal passes through the gate, and is inverted by it. From the gate, the signal passes to a 14-stage divider/counter IC2. The output from stage 4 (1.7Hz) is fed to a NAND logic gate, acting as a buffer to drive a light-emitting diode. This flases on and off whenever the Sun is shining and it is used when setting VR2. The output from stage 14 (0.00167Hz, or 1 pulse in 10 minutes) goes to a pair of decade counters, both in IC5. Thus the output changes once for every 10 minutes of sunshine and the 10-minute periods are counted by IC5. The output from the first counter of IC5, is decoded by IC6, which drives a 7-segment LED numeric display. The "8" output of the first counter goes to the second counter, which is decoded by IC7 and drives a second numeric display. The two displays show the number of completed 10-minute periods of sunshine, from 0 to 99. It is unlikely that the device will need to register a count higher than 99 (equivalent to 16½ hours of continuous sunshine). Even if it did and the count began again from zero, it would be obvious at the end of a long sunny day that 100 should be added to the reading.

The push-button S1 is used to reset the counters at the start of each measuring period.

Construction

Ideally the sensors would be a matched pair of LDRs but it is not normally possible to purchase such a pair. In practice, any pair of LDRs of the same type, preferably purchased at the same time from the same supplier, should be sufficiently alike in their characteristics. Measure the resistance of each LDR under the same illumination and select the one with the larger resistance as R3. Figure 2.8 shows the LDRs mounted on a piece of circuit board. The curved bar is made from matt black card or painted metal. The central part is long enough so that it can be bent into a semicircle, the centre of which is level with the upper surface of R4, with a section at each end to bring the slotted parts on to the side of the block. The width of the strip should be a few millimetres greater than the diameter of the LDR. A certain amount of experimentation may be needed to get the width just right — if it is too wide, it cuts out too much skylight; if it is too narrow, the array needs careful adjustment every day to shield R4 from direct sunlight. The leads from the sensor array to the main circuit can be several metres long, as changes in their resistance with temperature are insignificant compared with changes in the resistance of the LDRs.

The circuit is shown operating on a power supply of +6V DC but it works on any DC voltage in the range 5V to 15V. Increase the value of R4 — R17 to 560Ω for 15V operation. At 6V the supply current is approximately 30mA, most of which is required for the display. The amount of current can be reduced by blanking off the display except when needed; connect the blanking inputs of IC6 and IC7 as shown in Figure 2.9. This reduces operating current to about 8mA.

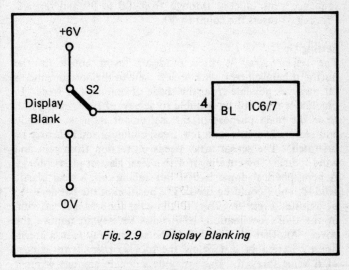

Fig. 2.9   Display Blanking

The first step is to build the sensor array and set it up temporarily by a window where it can receive direct sunlight. Wire up the sensing circuit (VR2, IC4). It is best to use a panel-mounted potentiometer for VR2 so that the sunny/cloudy level can be adjusted. Connect the sensor array to the sensing circuit and check its operation, adjusting VR2 to a suitable level.

Next build the clock; VR1 can be a preset potentiometer mounted on the circuit board since, once the timing is set, it seldom needs further adjustment. A small hole could be provided in the enclosure to allow a screw-driver to engage with VR1. Add IC3 and IC4 to the circuit, together with D1, S1 and R3. D1 flashes when the sensor array is in sunlight, but stays permanently on or off when it is cloudy. Pressing S1 resets the counter and turns D1 on.

Complete the circuit by wiring in IC5 – IC7, R4 – R17 and the LED displays. Note that the displays must be of the *common cathode* type. Altough 14 individual resistors may be used for R4 – R17, it is more convenient to use two packages of 7 commoned resistors. To check wiring, temporarily connect pin 9 of IC6 to pin 7 of IC2. The counting sequence runs quickly through from 00 to 99 and repeats. Pressing S1 resets the count to 00.

Setting Up

The sensor array is sited outdoors facing south (in the northern hemisphere), with a clear view to the horizon, and as far away as possible from the shade of buildings or trees. In practice it may not be possible to achieve the ideal siting but, since the main purpose of the instrument is to record daily and seasonal variations, a few trees, buildings and hills may be tolerated. The sensor array needs protection from rain and wind, possibly by covering it with a clear glass or plastic dome. A hemispherical dome is best but, failing this, a clear plastic sandwich-box could be used. The position of the bar needs to be adjusted every few days to allow for the seasonal variation in the Sun's declination, so it must be easy to remove the cover. Another place to locate the sensor array is in a greenhouse, preferably just below the roof so there is no danger of it being sprayed. There may be a certain amount of error when a cross-beam shades both sensors but such error is likely to be negligible.

The main circuit box is installed in a convenient place indoors, or possibly in the greenhouse. Adjust the clock rate before closing the box. The most accurate way of doing this is to wire the NAND gate and LED to output 9 (pin 12) of IC2. The signal from this has a frequency of 0.0533Hz, or one pulse in approximately 19s. Adjust VR1 until the time between the LED going out and the next time it goes out is exactly 19s. To give increased precision, connect the LED to output 12 (pin 1). Now re-adjust VR1 until the period of one pulse is 150s.

A bright day with blue sky and a reasonable amount of cloud and wind is best for finally setting up the circuit. When the Sun is shining, slide the bar until R4 is shaded by the bar. When cloud is covering the Sun, adjust VR2 until D1 flashes, *then* turn it until D1 just stops flashing. Press S1 to reset the counters; D1 comes on. When the Sun shines again, D1 begins flashing and continues until the Sun is clouded again. The display is incremented by '1' for every 10 minutes of sunshine. At dusk, record the reading for the day and press S1 to reset the instrument ready for the next day.

Details of Special Parts

Semiconductors
D1   Light emitting diode

Integrated Circuits
IC1   7555 CMOS timer
IC2   4020BE CMOS 14-stage divider/counter
IC3   4011BE CMOS quadruple 2-input NAND gate
IC4   ICL7611 CMOS operational amplifier (or similar)
IC5   4518BE CMOS dual decade counter
IC6, IC7   4511BE CMOS 7-segment latch and driver (2 off).

Chapter 3

THERMAL SENSORS

When a solid object is heated, the atoms or molecules of which it is composed move more vigorously and with increased amplitude. In a fluid the atoms are free to move individually and, when heated, move with increased velocity. In either case, heating increases the kinetic energy (the energy of motion) of the atoms or molecules. Temperature is a measure of the average kinetic energy of the atoms or molecules. If an object is heated at one point, the kinetic energy is gradually shared between the atoms or molecules until they all have an approximately equal share — the temperature of the object becomes uniform. The heat has been *conducted* to all parts of the object. The sharing of kinetic energy also occurs between an object and its surroundings. The usual technique for measuring the temperature of an object is to place a sensor in contact with it. The atoms or molecules of the object and of the sensor gradually share their energy equally, and the sensor acquires the temperature of the object. The measurement is then made. The same applies when we measure the temperature of a fluid (liquid or gas) enclosed in a container. In this instance, circulation of the fluid (*convection*) usually plays a part in the transfer of the heat.

There are two scales in use for the measurement of temperature. The everyday scale is the Celsius scale, on which the freezing point of water at standard atmospheric pressure is $0°C$, and the boiling point of water at standard atmospheric pressure is $100°C$. The scientific measure of temperature is the thermodynamic scale, often referred to as the kelvin scale. On this scale, 0K is absolute zero, equivalent to approximately $-273°C$. There is no temperature colder than this. On both scales an increase of one degree represents the same increase in temperature, so water freezes at 273K and boils at 373K. Note that we do not use the 'degree' symbol (°) when referring to kelvin.

There are circumstances when temperature have to be measured at a distance, for example, when measuring the temperature of a furnace. A sensor placed inside the furnace would be burned or melted. Instead of placing the sensor inside the furnace, we open the furnace door and measure the radiation emerging from it. The radiation from a very hot object consists of a mixture of wavelengths generated by the motion of the atoms or molecules of which it is composed. The mixture of wavelengths depends on temperature. Consider what happens when a very hot object is allowed to cool. At the beginning the object is exceedingly hot and the radiation includes UV, visible light and IR. As the object cools and the amount of agitation of its molecules decreases, and the shorter wavelengths gradually disappear from the radiation. As it continues to cool, the overall colour of the visible radiation changes from blue to white to red to dull red. As the object cools further, it ceases to emit UV and visible radiation but continues to emit in the IR bands. Thus, by measuring the radiation from an object and taking account of the wavelengths and their intensities, we can estimate the temperature of the object without actually having to place a sensor in contact with it. This is the basis of *pyrometry* ('fire-measuring'). Because pyrometry is essentially related to temperature measurement, we deal with pyrometers in this chapter rather than in Chapter 2.

Features to be considered when selecting a heat sensor for measuring the temperature of an object or inside a space include the following:

* *thermal or pyrometric?* — see discussion above;

* *range* — some sensors are insensitive or do not function at low temperatures; some are destroyed by excessively high temperatures;

* *physical size* — it is preferable for the sensing element to be small in relation to the size of the object or space;

* *thermal capacity* — if the sensing element has a large heat capacity, it alters the temperature of the object or space; this feature is partly related to that of physical size;

* *response time* — ideally the sensor should rapidly acquire the temperature of the object or space, and should closely follow all temperature changes;

* *linearity* — a linear response to temperature makes the processing circuit easier to design.

The range of thermal sensors includes the following, of which the last two are pyrometric:

1 Thermistor

A thermistor or *thermally sensitive resistor* consists of a sintered mixture of sulphides, selenides, or oxides of nickel, manganese, cobalt, copper, iron or uranium. The mixture is formed into a rod, a disc or a bead (Fig. 1.2), and may be bare or sealed in a glass or plastic capsule. The property of this mixture is that its resistivity decreases as temperature increases. The relationship between temperature and resistance is:

$$R_T = R_{ref}e^{-\beta(1/T - 1/T_{ref})}$$

R_T is the resistance in ohms at a given temperature T, expressed in kelvin, R_{ref} is the resistance at given reference temperature T_{ref}, usually 298K (25°C). The constant β depends on the material from which the thermistor is made. The constant, e, is the exponential constant, which has the value 2.718 to 3 decimal places. It can be seen from the equation that the relationship between resistance and temperature is not linear. However, over a limited range of temperature, the departure from linearity is often not of practical significance.

Thermistors operate over the temperature range −50°C to +300°C, making them useful in a variety of applications. Thermistors can be produced as small beads only about 0.5mm in diameter with very small thermal capacity and rapid response time. Their small size makes them suitable for measuring temperatures in confined spaces. For example, in medical studies they can be inserted in the human body, and in botanical investigations they have been used to measure the temperature *inside* the leaves of plants. In electronic circuits, thermistors are sometimes used to compensate for variations in ambient temperature.

One problem with using a thermistor is that it is necessary to pass a current through it in order to generate a p.d. across it. This current heats the thermistor, altering its resistance. This is a particularly serious difficulty with low-temperature measurements, or where high precision is required. Often the effect of self-heating can be avoided or minimised by appropriate circuit design, for instance by using a bridge circuit (Fig. 1.7) with the thermistor in arm AB and a compensating dummy thermistor in arm BC.

2 Bandgap sensor

This device depends upon two opposite voltage changes, both of which are temperature-dependent. One of these changes is produced by a single transistor for the base-emitter voltage (V_{BE}) of any transistor *decreases* with increase of temperature. The other change is produced by a pair of transistors wired so that they produce a voltage that *increases* with temperature. By choice of suitable resistors, the positive and negative voltage changes can be made to cancel out, so that a *constant* output voltage is obtained, which is independent of temperature. This is the basis of the *bandgap voltage reference*, used to obtain a precise voltage level in a circuit. By an extension of this principle it is possible to design a circuit in which the resultant voltage increases linearly with temperature by a prescribed amount. Such circuits are available in integrated form. For example, the LM35 precision temperature sensor, connected as in Figure 3.1 gives an output in the range 0V to 1.1V for temperatures in the range 0°C to 110°C, a voltage change of 10mV per degree Celsius. It can also be connected so as to operate over the range −40°C to 110°C, with an output of −0.04V to +1.1V. It has an accuracy of ±0.4°C at 25°C and ±0.8°C over its whole range. A welcome feature of this IC is that voltage is converted to temperature simply by multiplying by 100. The sensor can be connected directly to a voltmeter scaled to read up to 100mV and temperatures from 0°C to 100°C can be read directly. The LM35 has low thermal capacity and a fast response time.

A more elaborate IC, the LM3911, includes a comparator so that the temperature-dependent voltage can be matched against a pre-set voltage. This IC is used as a precision temperature controller for thermostats and similar systems.

3 Diode thermometer

This type of thermometer is based on the fact that conduction

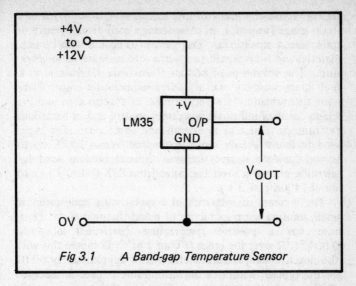

Fig 3.1   A Band-gap Temperature Sensor

through a semiconductor diode is temperature-dependent. The diode, usually a silicon or gallium-arsenide diode, is connected to a constant current source. The small size and mass of the diode results in a rapid time constant. Although they can be used over the range 1 to 400K, their sensitivity (i.e. change of current with temperature) is much greater below about 40K (about −200°C) so they are mainly used for low-temperature work.

4 Platinum resistance thermometer

The variation of resistance with the temperature of a coil of platinum wire is used as the basis of this type of thermometer. The resistivity of platinum is low, as with all metals, so an appreciable length of wire is required to give a resistance large enough to be measurable. The wire is usually coiled around a ceramic former, and often coated on the outside with ceramic material. The sensor is relatively large and massive (compared with a bead thermistor, for example), so has high thermal capacity and slow response time.

A more recent development is to print a narrow conductive track on an insulating base, using platinum ink. The track zig-zags across the insulator in a similar way to the track of a strain gauge (page 62), so compacting a considerable length of track into a small area. The element is coated with ceramic material and is cemented to a surface to measure its temperature. The advantage of platinum resistance thermometers is their great accuracy over a limited temperature range. Platinum thermometers are very robust in construction and are widely used in industrial processing control and in hazardous environments, such as in aircraft and spacecraft. The types used in industry have ranges extending from $-100°C$ up to several hundred degrees Celsius. Special versions used for scientific purposes cover the range from 83K ($-190°C$) up to about 1400K (1673°C).

The increase of resistance of a metal with temperature is small, limiting the responsivity of metal thermometers. Platinum has a positive temperature coefficient of only $0.004/°C/\Omega$ over the range 0°C to 100°C. Compare this with the negative temperature coefficient of approximately -0.01 for the typical thermistor shown in Table 1, page 3. Because of the small temperature coefficient, a sensitive processing circuit is essential. A bridge circuit (page 13) is the usual way of measuring resistance changes; often this includes dummy leads to compensate for resistance changes in the leads. Currents must be kept small, to avoid self-heating of the sensor.

Although platinum is the most frequently used metal, cheaper resistance thermometers with wires of nickel or nickel-alloy are sometimes used over restricted temperature ranges. Such devices are manufactured under the description of precision temperature-sensing resistors. The PRC100 is an example, with a coil made of an alloy of nickel, copper, manganese and iron. Its resistance rises in a linear fashion from 100Ω at 0°C to 138.5Ω at 100°. These figures exemplify the low temperature coefficients of such devices, and emphasise the need for precision processing circuits.

5 Thermocouple

When the junction of two dissimilar metals is heated, an e.m.f. is generated. This is known as the *Seebeck effect*, and the junction is called a *thermocouple*. Junctions are usually

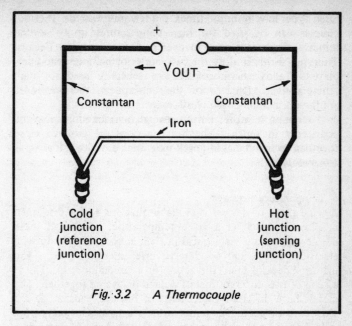

Fig. 3.2   *A Thermocouple*

formed by twisting the ends of two wires together and then welding them. For measuring temperature we connect two junctions, as shown in Figure 3.2. The *sensing junction*, sometimes called the *hot junction*, is at the temperature to be measured. The *reference junction*, alternatively known as the *cold junction*, is held at a reference temperature. The e.m.f. is proportional to the difference between the junction temperatures, and is measured by one of the techniques described on page 9. The size of the e.m.f. depends on the composition of the two wires. For example, the commonly used iron/constantan (copper-nickel alloy) thermocouple gives an output of 5.4mV when the cold junction is at $0°C$ and the hot junction is at $100°C$.

Output is reasonably linear over a wide range, allowing precise temperature measurements, but above a certain level, the e.m.f. falls off and may then decrease with increasing temperature. One of the advantages of thermocouples is that the junction can be very small, especially if it is a butt joint.

Such types have response times of a few milliseconds. Thermocouples can be used for high temperatures up to several hundred degrees or even to over a thousand degrees Celsius. Tungsten/rhenium alloy thermocouples or platinum/rhodium-platinum alloy thermocouples are generally used for high temperatures. Because of their cheapness, thermocouples are the most widely used of all temperature sensors.

To obtain a higher e.m.f., several thermocouples may be connected in series. The hot junctions are grouped close together, as are the cold junctions. Such a device is known as a *thermopile*.

6 Temperature switches

A wide range of devices is available that are designed to open or close a switch at a given temperature. Although these devices are purely mechanical in their action, they produce an electrical effect and so deserve brief mention here. The majority depend upon the action of a bimetallic strip. This is a strip of two different metals welded or riveted together. The metals have different coefficients of linear expansion, so the strip curls or uncurls as temperature changes. One end of the strip is fixed and the movement of the other end operates a snap-action switch. Such devices are used in thermostat circuits, for example for switching refrigerators on and off, and in fire-alarm circuits.

Another type of temperature switch has a sealed bulb containing a gas, and connected to a pressure transducer. Increased temperature causes an increase of gas pressure which is detected by the sensor and triggers the switch.

7 Radiation pyrometers

Radiation pyrometers are used for remote sensing of temperature, particularly when the temperature to be measured is that of a furnace or an exceedingly hot object. Although they are potentially sensitive to a wide range of radiation, filters are normally employed to restrict their operating range to the IR band. Such pyrometers can also be used for measuring temperatures below the 'red heat' or 'white heat' levels that we generally associate with pyrometry.

There are many types of pyrometer based on a variety of sensing elements including thermopiles, thermistors, pyro-electric sensors (see 8 below) or photovoltaic devices, all of which have been described in other sections. Different models of pyrometer combine particular features to suit them to a given application.

Pyrometers often have an optical system incorporating a telescope. This allows the user to aim the pyrometer accurately at the source of heat and to know what fraction of the field of view is filled by the object. A dichroic mirror in the optical system, while allowing visible light to pass to the telescope, reflects IR on to a sensor. The intensity of IR being received is a measure of the temperature of the object.

Some types of pyrometer work on a different principle which is related to that of the original 'disappearing filament' pyrometer. This operated in the visible light band. The telescope incorporated a lamp with a tungsten ribbon filament, located so that the user could see both the filament and the hot object (or open furnace door) at the same time. The brightness of light coming from the filament was varied by adjusting a resistor until the filament 'disappeared' against the background of the hot object or furnace. The filament was then at the same temperature as the hot object, and this could be determined by measuring the current through the filament, and using calibration charts. The electronic version of this type of pyrometer incorporates a light-chopping system, so that the sensor alternately receives infra-red radiation from the hot object and from the filament of a standard lamp situated inside the instrument. The current through the filament is varied automatically until the sensor is receiving radiation of equal intensity from either source and the output of the sensing circuit ceases to fluctuate in level. Calibration charts then give the temperature of the filament, from which the temperature of the hot object can be deduced.

Radiometers are similar in action to radiation pyrometers but calibrated to show the rate at which heat is reaching the sensor in unit time. They usually have a wider viewing angle than pyrometers and are used for investigating heat sources such as rocket exhausts, or the radiation from the Sun or from the whole sky ('global radiation'). The sensor in such an instrument is often a thermopile with the hot junctions facing toward the source of heat and the cold junctions facing toward the inside of the instrument.

Bolometers are used for the same purpose as pyrometers, that is for measuring temperature at a distance, but work on a slightly different principle. They do not detect the infra-red radiation directly, but by measuring its heating effect. Bolometers usually have a pair of matched thermistors, a sensing thermistor and a compensating thermistor, both mounted on a heat sink. The sensing thermistor is exposed to the source of radiation and is blackened to aid absorption. IR absorbed by the thermistor raises its temperature, causing the resistance of the thermistor to be reduced. The compensating thermistor allows for variations in ambient temperature. It is mounted on the same heat sink but shielded from radiation. The thermistors are wired into a bridge circuit (Fig. 1.7, arms AB and BC) the output of the bridge being proportional to the amount of radiation falling on the sensing thermistor.

8 Pyroelectric devices

These are radiation detectors which generate an e.m.f. measurable by circuits of the type described on page 9. Pyroelectric devices are sensitive to *the rate of change* in the intensity of thermal (IR) radiation reaching them rather than to the absolute level of radiation. The sensitive material in these devices consists of a crystal, or a plastic or ceramic substance that has been heated and then cooled while in a strong magnetic field. When it is subjected to a change in incident IR, an e.m.f. is generated between opposite surfaces of the material. The e.m.f. is generated in the bulk of the material, not at a junction as in the case of the thermocouple. Pyroelectric detectors are extremely sensitive to small changes in the amounts of IR falling on them. Their response time is less than 25ms.

When used as temperature-measuring devices, the pyroelectric device is subjected to the radiant energy from the object, chopped by passing it through a bladed fan. The rapid 'on—off' effect results in an alternating e.m.f. The amplitude of the wave signal from the sensor is then related to the measurand. Pyroelectric devices have entered the home extensively as the sensing elements in passive infra-red intruder detectors. A device such as the F001P, in which the sensitive material is lead-zirconate-titanate, is placed behind a special plastic 'lens' which is directed toward the area to be protected. The lens picks up and concentrates the IR being radiated from any warm object, including any person, in the area. The lens divides the area into fields so arranged that a person *moving* through the area frequently passes from one field to another. This causes rapid *changes* in the intensity of IR reaching the sensor, which generates an e.m.f. used to trigger the alarm. A project based on this sensor is described at the end of this chapter.

A pyroelectric sensor is also sensitive to vibration. In this way it acts like the piezo-electric crystal of a microphone (page 102). In an intruder system it is possible to use the same sensor to detect both IR and sound.

PROJECT 2 – Temperature Alarm (Level 1)

This is a simple but precise thermometer which operates in the range $0°C$ to $100°C$ and is correct to approximately 1 degree. Its special feature is that it can be set to sound an alarm if the temperature falls below or rises above a given level. The sensor is mounted on the case of the instrument or can be mounted externally at distance from it. The temperature alarm has many applications around the home. Applications for which it detects excess temperature include detection of fire, fat-fire (installed over the cooker), greenhouse overheating, and electric fires being left on unnecessarily. As a detector of unduly low temperature, it warns against outdoor frost, windows or doors being accidentally left open in cold weather, and low temperature in rooms occupied by elderly or infirm persons.

How It Works
The sensor is one of the band-gap detectors described in Section 2 above. In the circuit of Figure 3.3 the sensor is wired to give an output which ranges from 0V to 1V as the temperature varies from $0°C$ to $100°C$. Z1 is a band-gap voltage reference device which produces a constant 2.5V at

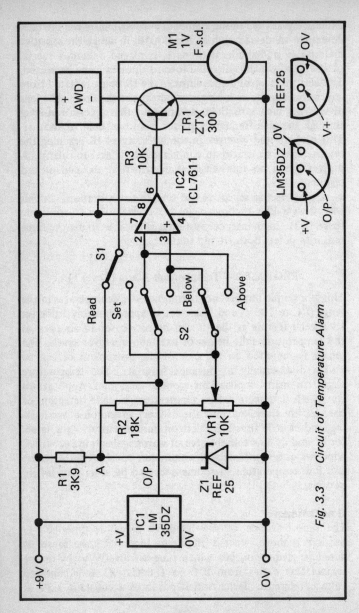

Fig. 3.3 Circuit of Temperature Alarm

point A. Both the voltage from the sensor and that from Z1 are independent of battery voltage until it has fallen to about 8V.

The 2.5V from the reference is applied to a potential-divider consisting of R2 and VR1. The voltage tapped at the wiper of VR1 can be set to any voltage in the range 0V to just over 1V. Thus we produce a standard voltage to set the level at which the alarm sounds.

For simplicity we use a moving-coil meter or digital panel meter to display the output voltage from the sensor. A 1V moving-coil meter can very conveniently have its scale marked in degrees Celsius. The meter is also used to display the alarm temperature level by switching S1 to connect the meter to the wiper of VR1.

The voltages from the sensor and VR1 are compared by an operational amplifier, IC2. S2 is connected as a reversing switch so that the sensor output goes to the (−) input of the amplifier and the voltage from VR1 goes to the (+) input, or the other way about. If the sensor output is switched to the (−) input, the output of the amplifier is normally low, but swings high and sounds the alarm if the temperature falls below the pre-set level. If the sensor output is switched to the (+) input, the alarm sounds if the pre-set temperature is exceeded.

The audible warning device is one of the solid-state type which produces a powerful tone when a current is passed through it. In this circuit TR1 acts as a switch, turning on the current when the output from IC2 goes high. AWDs can be obtained which produce a two-tone note when energised. The sound from these is much more likely to catch attention than that from the simpler single-tone AWD. For the more light-hearted applications, musical buzzers are available to play a sequence of popular tunes when activated.

Construction

The unit takes only about 2mA when quiescent, so it can easily be powered from a PP3 9V battery. It can be housed in a small case, possibly one with a built-in battery compartment. Before beginning construction, and deciding on the size and shape of the case, it is important to consider what type of meter is to be used. A moving-coil meter is the easiest to use and install. Since 1V f.s.d. is required to cover the full range of the sensor, the simplest solution is to purchase a 100μA meter and to wire this in series with a 10kΩ resistor. The resistor should have 1% tolerance or less. An alternative type of meter is the digital panel meter with liquid crystal display. These are available as ready-built units and usually require the addition of two external resistors to set the full-scale range. Refer to the instruction leaflet supplied with the meter for details of how to connect and calibrate it. As well as space for the meter, there must be room on the panel for two toggle switches and VR1, and for a third toggle switch for the power supply if required.

The circuit is easily assembled on a small piece of circuit-board. The sensor may be mounted on the board, preferably arranged so that it lies close to a number of ventilating holes drilled in the case. For greater sensitivity, mount it with the body of the sensor protruding from the case. If remote reading is required, solder it to a 3-core lead with a plug fitting into a socket on the case. The AWD may also be mounted on the board but produces a louder sound if firmly secured to the outside of the case. It may also be mounted at a distance from the main unit, depending on the applications intended. Connection to the battery is by a PP3 battery connector.

To test the unit, connect or switch on the power supply; put S1 to 'Read' and S2 to 'Below'. Turn VR1 toward the 0V end of its scale. The meter indicates the room tempera-ture. Grip the sensor between finger and thumb; the reading increases by a few degrees. If the circuit appears to be faulty, check the voltage at the output of IC1; at normal room temperature (25°C) this should read 0.25V. Change S1 to 'Set'; turn VR1 and watch the meter reading vary from 0V to 1V, or slightly more. The AWD sounds when the reading exceeds room temperature. If it does not reach 1V, check that voltage at A is 2.5V, reduce R2 until the full 0−1V is obtainable at the wiper of VR1 and at the meter. Change S1 to 'Above' and check that the AWD sounds when VR1 is turned to bring the reading below room temperature.

Using the Temperature Alarm

If you do not wish to use the alarm, put S1 to 'Set', S2 to 'Below', turn VR1 so that the reading is 0°C, and finally put S1 to 'Read'. The instrument then displays the temperature and the alarm will not sound. To set the alarm, switch S2 to 'Above' or 'Below', then put S1 to 'Set' and adjust VR1 until the required alarm temperature is displayed. Put S1 to 'Read'. The instrument displays the current temperature and the alarm sounds when it exceeds or is less than the pre-set level.

Details of Special Parts

Integrated circuits
IC1 LM35DZ precision Celsius (centigrade) temperature sensor; the more expensive and slightly more precise LM35CZ may be used instead.
IC2 REF25 precision band-gap voltage reference; similar devices such as the ZNREF025C1 can be used instead.
IC3 ICL7611DCPA CMOS operational amplifier; the CA3140 can be used instead, with pin 8 unconnected.

Miscellaneous
AWD — almost any type operating on 3–16V DC.

PROJECT 3 – Passive Infra-Red Intruder Detector (Level 2)

An active infra-red intruder detector system is one in which a beam of IR is directed at a sensor. When the beam is broken the alarm sounds. Such a system actively produces IR. A passive IR system such as this project relies on detecting the IR produced by the intruder. To detect the very small amount of IR emitted by a human body several metres away requires a very sensitive detector. This project uses a pyroelectric sensor, as described in Section 8 above. It can detect a person at a range of up to 12 metres. When the intruder is detected, an alarm sounds and continues to sound until the system is reset. The circuit can also be used to operate a courtesy lamp in a hallway or porch, turning on the lamp automatically when anyone enters the area.

How It Works

As mentioned in Section 8, the pyroelectric detector responds to *changes* in the level of IR reaching it. A change such as that resulting from a person entering the room is sufficient to cause the sensor to respond, but the chances of detection are greatly improved by using a special lens to collect the IR and focus it on the detector. Not only does this concentrate the IR on to the sensor, but it divides the room into a number of zones. The lens is really a number of separate lenses moulded in a film of plastic, each lens directed to cover a narrow zone of the room (Fig. 3.4). At each of the four levels shown in the

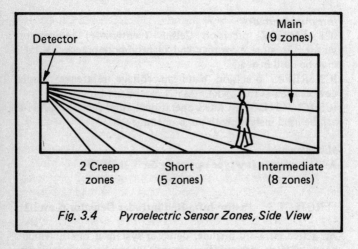

Fig. 3.4   *Pyroelectric Sensor Zones, Side View*

figure there are a number of zones radiating horizontally, covering an angle of 120°, dividing the room into 24 zones altogether. As the intruder moves around the room, he or she is constantly moving out of the view of one lens and, an instant later, into the field of view of another. Movement from zone to zone means that the amount of IR reaching the sensor rises and falls rapidly. In this way the lens increases the size of the e.m.f. produced.

The sensor recommended for this project consists of two pyroelectric devices mounted side-by-side, and connected in the opposite sense, thus further increasing the e.m.f. produced.

This e.m.f. is applied to the gate of a field effect transistor inside the sensor. There is also an internal gate resistor (Fig. 3.5). An external source resistor R1 is connected so that the FET is in source follower mode. Changes in e.m.f. generated by the sensor appear as a changing voltage across R1. As might be expected, the voltage changes are very small and need to be amplified. IC1 and IC2 are connected as inverting amplifiers each with a gain of 100. In the absence of any change in IR, the output of IC2 hovers close to 0V. When a person moves about in front of the sensor, or even stands still waving an arm, the voltage swings violently, often reaching +6V and −6V.

IC3 is wired as a comparator. The reference voltage is provided by VR1. This is set to a level between about +2V and +5V. Normally the output from IC2 is less than this, so the output of IC3 is +6V. When IR is detected, any positive swing of the IC2 output which exceeds the reference voltage causes the output of IC3 to fall sharply to −6V. VR1 can be set so that the circuit is triggered when the voltage from IC2 exceeds a pre-determined level, so it controls the sensitivity of the circuit.

The next stage is a flip-flop, consisting of 2 NAND gates in IC4. The two inputs to the flip-flop are normally held high, since the output of IC3 is high and R7 holds the other input high. The flip-flop is reset by pressing S2, and pin 11 goes high. This output is inverted by the third NAND gate, so its output is low. TR1 is off and the AWD is silent. When IR is detected the output of IC3 goes low, setting the flip-flop. Pin 11 goes low, causing the output of the third gate to go high, turning on the transistor and making the AWD sound. The large-value capacitor C3 acts as a delay. When S1 is pressed to reset the flip-flop, C3 is discharged. After S2 is released, C3 charges slowly through R7, taking about 40 seconds. This gives the operator time to get well clear of the detector after resetting it, before it becomes activated.

Construction

The circuit requires a dual power supply, provided by two 6V batteries or by two sets of four AA cells in battery holders. A double-pole single-throw toggle switch S1 is wired into the

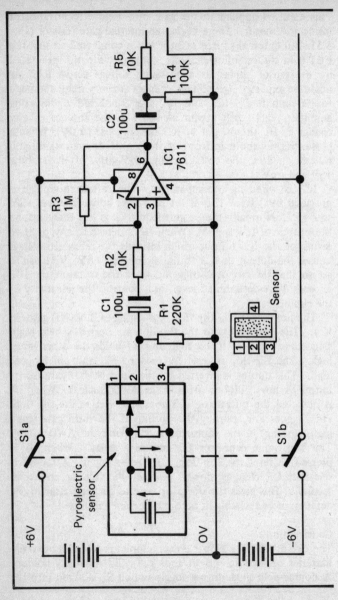

56

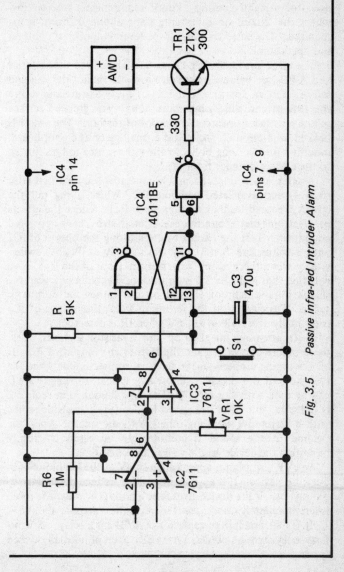

Fig. 3.5   Passive infra-red Intruder Alarm

positive and negative rails. The use of batteries has the advantage that the detector can be mounted on a wall without the need for unsightly wiring. Power requirements are very low when the circuit is quiescent, only about 0.25mA being required. The batteries will last for several months of continuous operation.

The enclosure needs to be large enough to hold the batteries and AWD (see below) and to give room to mount the lens and sensor. Cut an aperture in the lid of the enclosure and secure the lens behind this, using short bolts. The grooved surface of the lens faces toward the interior of the box. The sensor is held in an 8-pin d.i.l. socket on a small piece of circuit-board, mounted on two long bolts, to allow the sensor to be adjusted to the correct distance from the lens.

Assemble the amplifier and comparator sections first (IC1 to IC3) and associated components. When laying out the circuit, keep all leads as short as possible, to reduce the effects of electromagnetic interference from nearby mains-powered equipment. Test the circuit by monitoring the output of IC2 with a voltmeter. It normally stays steady at 0V, but swings widely when there is any movement in front of the lens. You will find that if the device is on the workbench beside you, the slightest movement of a hand or arm causes the output to swing. Depending on the setting of VR1, the output of IC3 is normally +6V, falling to −6V when IR is detected.

Next assemble the flip-flop and transistor sections. Test these before connecting the flip-flop to the output of IC3. If all is working properly, make the final connection between the two parts of the circuit. Almost any type of solid-state AWD can be used with this circuit. The type described in Project 2 is suitable, but there are other louder types available, some with a distinctive warbling tone. With the smaller types, the volume of the sound is considerably increased by firmly mounting the device on the wall of the enclosure.

Set VR1 to obtain approximately 4V at the (+) pin of IC3. Test the device. If it appears insensitive, reduce the voltage to 3V or less. If the device gives false alarms (i.e. when the room is left *completely unoccupied*) increase the voltage to about 5V.

It is also possible to replace the AWD by a relay. A light-duty relay may be used as a normally-open or normally-closed switch and wired into a more comprehensive security system. A relay with contacts rated for mains voltage may be used to switch on a courtesy lamp. In this application it is better to use a lens with a 'curtain' field. This is not downwardly-directed so that small animals can pass by without triggering the system. Readers are warned that adapting the circuit for mains use makes it a Level 3 project, suitable only for advanced constructors. It is not recommended for beginners or for those with little knowledge or experience of working with mains wiring and voltages.

In use as an intruder detector, the unit is mounted on the wall, preferably about 2m above floor level. It should be located so that it faces along the room rather than across it, or along a corridor or hallway. It must not be possible for an intruder to approach it from the side to disable it.

Details of Special Parts
The sensor used in the project was supplied by Electromail Ltd (see address on page 177) as a kit (Stock No. 256-275) containing the sensor itself and two lenses, volumetric and curtain. Other pyroelectric sensors are available and most may be used in this project but, without a lens, the range may be restricted to 2–3 metres.

Integrated circuits
IC1–IC3   ICL7611 CMOS operational amplifier
IC4   4011BE CMOS quadruple 2-input NAND gate.

Chapter 4

MECHANICAL FORCE SENSORS

The measurement of force is common to such diverse activities as weighing out a kilogram of meat, testing the breaking strength of a sample of ship's cable, designing earthquake-proof buildings, determining the air-speed of an aeroplane and evaluating the effectiveness of adhesives.

One of the main methods of force measurement involves measuring the amount by which a solid object is deformed (*strained*) when it is subjected to a force (*stress*). For this purpose a number of types of strain gauge have been developed. Another aspect of measuring force is in terms of force per unit area, or *pressure*. We may often need to measure this in liquids and in gases, including atmospheric pressure. Finally, because the unit of force, the newton, is defined as the amount of force that produces an acceleration of 1 m s^{-2} in a body of mass 1kg, we can measure force by measuring the acceleration it produces. This technique applies particularly to rapidly-changing force. There are a number of devices, known as *accelerometers* which are used to measure force in this way. We now consider strain gauges, pressure sensors and accelerometers under their respective headings.

1 Strain gauges

The metal-foil strain gauge consists of a thin metal foil produced by photo-etching so as to make a zig-zagging pattern of parallel conductors, as in Figure 4.1. The foil is supported on an insulating backing. The gauge is cemented to the object that is to be put under stress, so that the axis along which the conductors lie is parallel with the direction of greatest strain.

The resistance of a conductor is given by the equation:

$$R = \rho L/A$$

where ρ is the resistivity of the metal, L is its length and A its cross-sectional area. When the object to which the gauge is attached is strained by an applied force, the gauge is strained

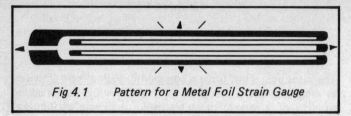

Fig 4.1   Pattern for a Metal Foil Strain Gauge

by the same proportionate amount. The conducting tracks become longer (L increases) and, to maintain a constant volume of material, the cross-sectional area A decreases. The effect of this is to increase the ratio L/A and hence increase the resistance of the gauge. If the gauge is subjected to a force that compresses it along its axis, the reverse applies and its resistance decreases. The effect is linear in either direction.

In certain other types of strain gauge, especially those made of semi-conducting materials, the action of strain is to increase the resistivity ρ of the material. This is known as the *piezo-resistive* effect and has the same result, increasing the resistance of the gauge. The disadvantages of semiconductor strain gauges is that they are not suitable for use at high temperatures. They tend to be fragile and difficult to apply.

The output of a strain gauge depends on a characteristic known as its *gauge factor*, a measure of its sensitivity. The gauge factor is calculated as:

$$\frac{\text{change in resistance}}{\text{resistance}} \times \frac{\text{length}}{\text{change in length}}$$

In other words, the gauge factor is the fractional change in resistance per fractional change in length. Gauge factors of 2 to 5 are typical of metal foil strain gauges, while those of semi-conductor gauges are higher, in the region 50–200. Given that the maximum strain that the gauge can be subjected to must not be more than a 3% to 4% extension of its length, the proportionate change in resistance of a strain gauge under measurable forces is not large.

We usually measure the resistance change using one of the bridge methods (page 13). The most sensitive is the full bridge

(Fig. 1.8(c)), in which 1 pair of gauges operates in the opposite sense to the other pair. One way of achieving this for measuring the strain on a beam is shown in Figure 4.2. The pair above the beam operates in the opposite sense to the pair below it.

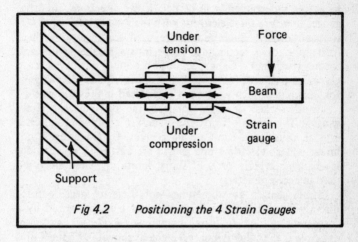

Fig 4.2   Positioning the 4 Strain Gauges

One of the possible errors with using strain gauges is that their resistance varies with temperature. Another problem is the possible generation of an e.m.f. at their junction with their leads, because of the Seebeck thermoelectric effect (page 44). For this reason, metal strain gauges are often made from constantan, a copper-nickel alloy with high resistivity, a high gauge factor, low temperature coefficient of resistance, and a minimum thermoelectric potential at the junction with the leads. Other alloys are often used for special purposes, such as operation at high temperatures.

An additional source of temperature error occurs when the object under stress is of metal. The object itself expands or contracts because of temperature changes. This forces the gauge to expand or contract too, altering its resistance. This effect can be compensated for in the design of the foil pattern. Strain gauges are available compensated for attachment to particular metals, including stainless steel, mild steel and aluminium.

In addition to the simple strain gauge pattern of Figure 4.1, gauges are made in a wide variety of other designs. In some there are two elements arranged perpendicularly to each other. Connected in series they register strain in all directions; connected to separate bridges, they allow for strain to be measured independently in perpendicular directions. In other gauges there are three elements with their axes at 45° or at 60° to each other. Such gauges are used for measuring shear (distortion of a rectangular shape into a parallelogram) and torque (twisting). Gauges are also produced with even more elaborate patterns, for detecting strain in circular diaphragms, for example. Such gauges are often used in pressure sensors.

Another class of strain gauge is the piezo-electric strain gauge. The strain distorts the structure of the piezo-electric crystal, causing an e.m.f. to be generated. The effect is not linear. Piezo-electric strain gauges are best used where strain is changing rapidly or is of short duration. They are often used in accelerometers.

Strain gauges are sometimes not used to measure force directly but to measure force that has been converted by a force sensing element, often known as a *load cell*. A typical example is the solid cylindrical element shown in Figure 4.3(a) which could be used in measuring the weight (force due to gravity) of a vehicle. The element supports a platform on to which the vehicle is driven. The weight of the vehicle (and platform) strains the element by an amount proportionate to the weight (the stress). Gauges mounted on the load cell measure the strain and, from this, the weight of the vehicle can be calculated. Figure 4.4 shows a load cell for measuring tension. This type is often known as a proving ring. It can be incorporated in the cable of a crane so that the load is measured while being lifted by the crane. The distortion of the ring under load can also be measured by means of an LVDT (Fig. 4.5) instead of a strain gauge.

An entirely different principle for measuring strain is the interferometer shown in Figure 4.6. A beam from a laser is split so that part of it goes to a reflector attached to the member that is undergoing strain. The reflected beam is combined with the original beam and the two beams fall on a screen, causing an interference pattern. The pattern consists

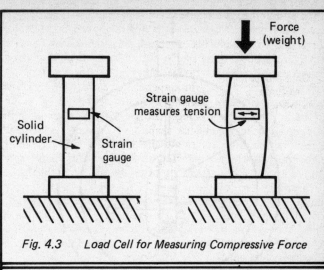

Fig. 4.3   Load Cell for Measuring Compressive Force

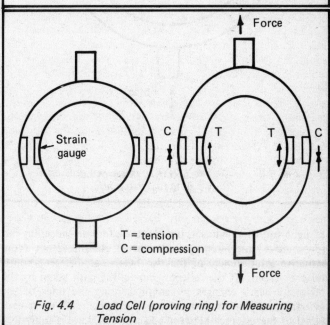

T = tension
C = compression

Fig. 4.4   Load Cell (proving ring) for Measuring Tension

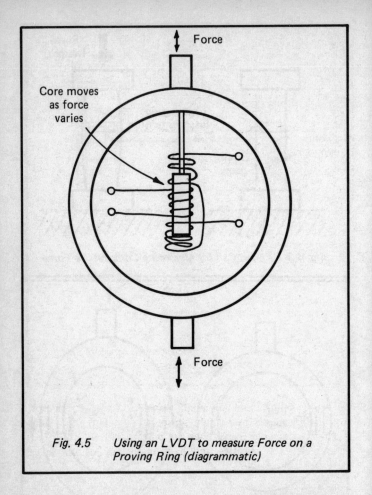

Force

Core moves
as force
varies

Force

*Fig. 4.5   Using an LVDT to measure Force on a
Proving Ring (diagrammatic)*

of light and dark bands, caused by the alternate cancelling-out
(destructive interference) and mutual reinforcement (con-
structive interference) of the two beams, at different points
on the screen. If the reflector moves, the path taken by the
reflected beam changes in length, causing the lines of the
interference pattern to move on the screen. A movement
equal to the distance between adjacent dark lines is equivalent

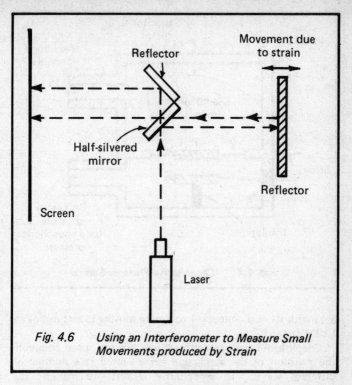

Fig. 4.6   Using an Interferometer to Measure Small Movements produced by Strain

to a movement of one half a light wavelength by the reflector. Automatic circuits use a light sensor to detect the dark lines and count by how many lines the pattern moves. Interferometers are very sensitive and have many applications apart from measuring strain.

2 Pressure sensors

Pressure sensors are used primarily for measuring pressure in liquids and gases, but they also are used in measuring fluid flow, as explained in Chapter 9. Pressure sensors usually depend upon sensing the movement of a diaphragm which has the measurand pressure on one side and a standard pressure on the other. We also use sensors such as the Bourdon tube (Fig.

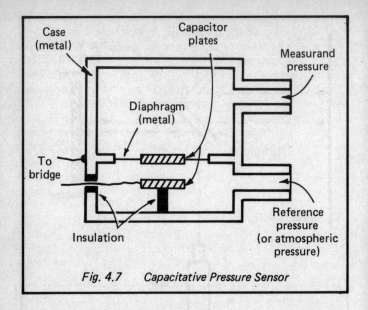

Fig. 4.7 *Capacitative Pressure Sensor*

1.1) with its end connected to a core moving in and out of an LVDT (page 17).

Diaphragm-based pressure sensors are the more common, the position of the diaphragm being sensed in a number of different ways. In *capacitative* sensors, we measure the capacitance between a plate attached to the diaphragm and a fixed plate (Fig. 4.7). Capacitance is inversely proportional to the distance between the plates and can be measured using a bridge (Fig. 1.10). In *inductive* sensors, the diaphragm is made of a ferromagnetic metal and a coil is placed near to it. Changes in the position of the diaphragm cause changes in the self-inductance of the coil. This can be measured using a bridge circuit. Another method of pressure-sensing is to cement a special *strain gauge* to the diaphragm to measure its distension. Better still, the diaphragm may be made of silicon with the strain-gauge conductors diffused into its surface. Such strain-gauges can be manufactured by similar techniques to those used for making integrated circuits. A complete 4-arm strain-gauge bridge is produced on a silicon diaphragm.

The gauge is usually piezo-resistive (see above). The bridge output is very nearly linear and a typical sensor gives 0.6mV for each kilopascal of pressure, over the range 0 to 100kPa (100kPa is approximately one atmosphere). Its main disadvantage is that the output falls by 0.19% for each degree Celsius rise in temperature, so compensation may be needed in some applications. Some pressure-sensor ICs have a built-in thermistor for this purpose.

Piezo-electric pressure sensors have a diaphragm behind which is mounted a crystal sensitive to pressure. Such sensors are used for measuring high-frequency pressure changes. Their action is very similar to that of an ordinary crystal microphone.

3 Accelerometers

Figure 4.8 illustrates the principle on which most accelerometers work. A mass, known as the *seismic mass* is held in position by springs. There may also be dampers to reduce the

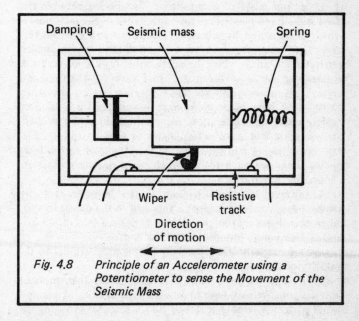

Fig. 4.8   *Principle of an Accelerometer using a Potentiometer to sense the Movement of the Seismic Mass*

amount of oscillation after the mass has been disturbed. When a force is applied to the case of the instrument, the case moves, but inertia of the mass results in it moving relative to the case. When the accelerating force is removed the springs return the mass to its former position within the case. During the period of acceleration the displacement of the mass from its resting position in the case depends on the size of the accelerating force. The displacement of the mass is measured by electronic sensors.

In the figure we show how we can use a potentiometric sensor. The mass is linked to the wiper of a potentiometer so that its movement makes the wiper move along the resistive track. A varying voltage appears at the wiper. The movement of the seismic mass can also be monitored by attaching it to an LVDT (page 17), or we can use a strain gauge.

There are several other ways in which the displacement of the mass can be measured. In capacitative accelerometers, the mass is mounted on a diaphragm, and may be disc-shaped itself to act as one plate of a capacitor. The spacing between the mass and a fixed plate alters the capacitance of the instrument, which is measured by a bridge. Piezo-electric accelerometers have the mass attached to a piezo-electric crystal which generates an e.m.f. when the accelerating crystal exerts force against the inertia of the mass. In Figure 4.9 the mass and crystal are disc-shaped and held together by an insulating bolt. This type of accelerometer is suitable for measuring rapidly changing acceleration, such as is produced by mechanical vibration and shock. The testing of vehicles and machinery, crash-testing and investigating the effects of earthquakes on buildings are all fields in which piezo-electric sensors are commonly employed.

A different principle is used in the inductive velocity sensor. A permanent magnet is attached to the object so that, when the object moves, the magnet is pushed into or out of a coil. The e.m.f. induced in a coil depends on the *rate of change* of magnetic field, so the e.m.f. is proportional to the velocity of the object.

Sometimes we need only to detect, rather than measure acceleration. We may wish to detect sudden shock, for example when a thief attempts to break into a shop by smashing the

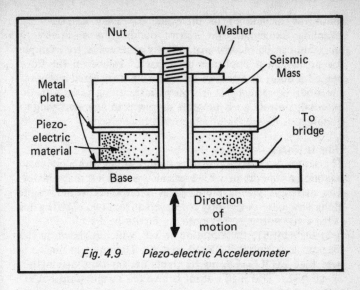

Fig. 4.9   Piezo-electric Accelerometer

window. For this purpose we use a vibration detector. One form of this has two strips of springy metal normally pressing against each other to maintain contact. The strips form a switch which is wired into an electronic alarm circuit. A seismic mass is mounted on one of the strips and, when the unit is accelerated by shock, the inertia of the mass causes the strips to become momentarily separated. This causes a break in electrical contact and the alarm is triggered.

Another type of vibration sensor has two electrodes sealed into a capsule partly filled with mercury. When the sensor is still, the mercury settles between the electrodes, making electrical contact between them. When the sensor is vibrated the mercury is disturbed, causing contact to be made and broken repeatedly. The breaking of contact is detected by an electronic circuit.

PROJECT 4 – Car/Bicycle Alarm (Level 1)

This circuit sounds an alarm whenever it detects vibration. It is a small portable device that can easily be hiden in the glove locker of a car or in a bicycle bag. When anyone attempts to

71

move the bicycle or to drive the car away without first disabling the circuit, the alarm sounds. Its sensitivity to vibration can be made use of in many other ways, for example for protecting a brief-case or luggage. Placed on the floor behind a door, or attached to a door, it is triggered whenever the door is opened. It is housed in a strong case, with no external controls, so it presents problems to anyone trying to disable it.

How It Works

The sensor is a vibration-sensing switch, either with a mercury-containing capsule, or with a seismic mass on a spring contact. The mercury type is preferred as it responds to movement along any axis. A flip-flop constructed from two NAND gates (Fig. 4.10) normally has both its inputs held high. Pin 1 is held high by S1, the vibration switch, which is shown in the diagram as a normally-closed switch. The input to pin 13 is held high by R2. Closing S2 resets the flip-flop, making pin 11 go high. This high output is inverted by the third NAND gate, and pin 10 goes low. Thus there is no base current to TR1, which is held off. No current flows through the audible warning device (AWD).

When vibration occurs, S1 opens briefly, allowing R1 to pull down the input at pin 1 to a low level. This sets the flip-flop. Pin 11 goes low, pin 10 goes high, the transistor is turned on and the AWD sounds. Once the flip-flop is set it remains in that state, with the alarm sounding until it is reset by closing S2. A switch or push-button on the case of the unit would make it too easy for the thief to silence the alarm. Instead, we hide S2 *inside* the case. For S2 we use a magnetic proximity switch (see Chapter 7). The switch is located inside the case in a position known only to the user. To reset the circuit all that is necessary is to close S2 briefly by touching a magnet to the outside of the case at the secret location. The magnet may then be removed and the device stays silent until the next disturbance. If the magnet is left against the outside of the case, it holds the circuit temporarily disabled.

Closing S2 discharges C1. When S2 is opened, C1 charges slowly through R2, and acts as a delay. It takes about 15 seconds to recharge, during which time the alarm can not be

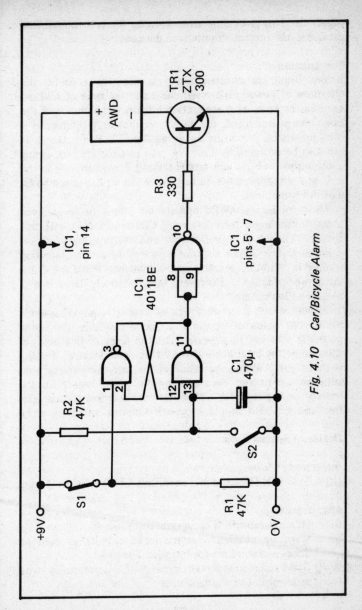

Fig. 4.10 Car/Bicycle Alarm

73

triggered. This gives time after resetting for you to leave the car or bicycle and for vibrations to die away.

Construction
Before beginning construction you need to consider the questions of power supply switching and the type of AWD to be used, as both of these factors influence the choice of the case. When quiescent, the circuit requires only 0.4mA, so it runs for about 2 months on an alkaline 9V PP3 battery. It can also be powered by four AA cells in a battery box, giving a 6V supply, which will last for about 6 months. Open the case and disconnect the battery when the device is not to be used for some time.

Most solid-state AWDs operate on 20mA or less. Even some of the larger (and louder) AWDs can be used with this circuit. Their high sound output and the possibility of programming such AWDs to emit a variety of attention-getting wailing or warbling sounds, means that they make the alarm far more effective. However, their relatively large size is usually a disadvantage.

Having decided on what size of case is required, select a robust one made of plastic — a metal case does not allow magnetic switches to operate. Drill an array of fine holes in the side of the case where the AWD is to be located. Fix the switches and AWD to the inside of the case using epoxy resin adhesive. You also need to supply a secure holder for the battery or battery box. When the circuit-board is complete, this can be held in place by self-adhesive mounting strip.

Details of Special Parts

Integrated circuit
IC1   4011BE CMOS quadruple 2-input NAND gate

Miscellaneous
S1   Mercury-capsule or spring vibration switch
S2   Magnetic proximity switch (reed switch), as used on doors and windows for intruder detection
AWD Solid state sounder or siren, 9—12V, preferably with intermittent or warbling note.

Chapter 5

POSITION AND PROXIMITY SENSORS

This chapter is about sensors and sensing techniques used to determine the position of an object in relation to its surroundings. Position is taken to include not only *location*, for example the instantaneous position of a bullet fired from a gun under test, and *angular position*, for example the amount by which a shaft has turned, but also *attitude*, for example the direction in which a pipeline is being laid. Linear and angular position are sometimes referred to as linear and angular *displacement*. In all of these the position is measured relative to a framework. The framework may be on the small scale, for example with reference to some fixed point on the machine of which the moving object is part. Or we may refer to a large-scale framework, such as the grid of lines of latitude and longitude of the Earth's surface. Angular measurements may be taken relative to the fixed direction of some part of a machine or, as an example on the larger scale, relative to the direction of magnetic North.

Proximity is a measure of linear position in the limited sense that we are concerned only with the position of the object when it is less than a given distance from the sensor or some other fixed point. We are sensing 'nearness' or, more often, the state of being 'too near'. Position sensors often have a physical connection with the object, but proximity sensors almost all operate remotely with no connection other than that provided by a beam of IR, a beam of ultra-sound or the effect at a distance on a magnetic or electrical field. Those position sensors that operate remotely may also be used as proximity detectors if their output is adapted to produce an on—off signal.

Of the many types of position and proximity sensor that have been invented, we have space here to deal with only a few of the more widely used ones.

1 Linear potentiometer
This is perhaps one of the most straightforward types of position

sensor. A linear potentiometer is used when the object whose position is to be sensed is free to move along only one axis. The potentiometer is usually very similar to the variable resistor used as a 'slider' volume control in audio equipment. It consists of a strip of resistive material, such as a carbon track, with a sliding wiper that can be moved from one end of the track to the other. The wiper is attached to the moving object and the voltage at the wiper varies from 0V to V_{IN} as the object travels over its full range. A voltage-measuring circuit (page 9) reads and displays the object's position.

An example of the use of a linear potentiometer was described in Chapter 4, where it sensed the position of the seismic mass in an accelerometer (Fig. 4.8). In that application the position signal is processed electronically to convert it into an acceleration signal, using circuits described in Chapter 10.

One limitation of the potentiometer is that the extent of moving is usually limited to a few centimetres. Another problem is that the wiper inevitably offers a certain amount of frictional resistance to the free movement of the object, so this technique is suitable only when the forces moving the object are relatively large. Advantages are that the voltages involved are large enough to be easily measurable, and that V_{OUT} is linearly related to position. However, carbon tracks eventually wear, causing unevenness and non-linearity. A flat coil of resistance wire is better, though it must be fine wire if the device is to have good resolution. A cermet track, consisting of a metal-containing ceramic, is often used to combine reliability with durability.

The potentiometer principle is also applied to sensing angular position. For this we use a rotary potentiometer very similar to those used as rotary volume controls in audio equipment. Low-cost computer joysticks often have two rotary potentiometers to sense the rotation of the joystick about two perpendicular axes.

2 Linear variable differential transformer

The principle of the LVDT was described on page 17. This device has very many applications in position sensing. The LVDT is reliable and easy to use and has found many applications where the measurand is not *position*, as such. For example, an LVDT is used in the proving ring of Figure 4.5 to sense the position of the top of the ring relative to the bottom of the ring, and hence the force that is distorting the ring.

A sensor related to the LVDT is the rotary variable differential transformer (RVDT), an example of which is illustrated in Figure 5.1. It is used for measuring angular displacement over a limited range.

Both LVDTs and RVDTs rely on varying the *reluctance*, the degree of coupling between coils. Sensors which depend on another electromagnetic property, *inductance*, are described in the next section. Reluctance is the equivalent of resistance, only in a magnetic circuit instead of in an electrical circuit. In Figure 5.1 the core is rotated toward the left so the coupling between the central (primary) coil and the left-hand (secondary) coil is greater than that between central coil and that on the right. On the right, the gap between the end of the movable core and the fixed core of the right-hand coil is a volume through which magnetic lines of force do not easily pass — it is the equivalent of resistance. In terms of magnetic resistance, the magnetic resistance of the magnetic circuit comprising the central and left-hand coil is less than that of the circuit comprising the central and right-hand coil. As the core is rotated, the magnetic resistances change relative to each other, increasing or decreasing the current induced in the secondary coils. The coils are connected so that V_{OUT} is zero when the core is central, and increases as the core is rotated to the right or to the left. In one direction the alternating output voltage is in phase with the input voltage. In the other direction it is $180°$ out of phase. A phase-dependent circuit is used to distinguish between rotation to the right and to the left. Over a reasonably large range, V_{OUT} is linearly proportional to the position of the core.

LVDTs and RVDTs are two types of reluctive sensor in common use, but there are many variants that rely on the same principle. One of these is described in the next section.

3 Synchro systems
These are used for sensing position. The synchro system (Fig. 5.2) consists of a transmitter and a receiver. In the transmitter there is a rotor or primary coil, the position of which is to be

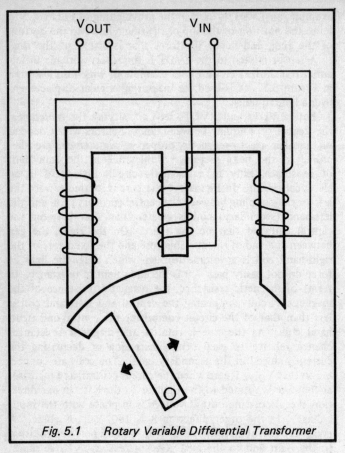

Fig. 5.1 Rotary Variable Differential Transformer

sensed. An alternating current is sent through the rotor coil, inducing currents in the three stator or secondary coils around it. The receiver also has a primary rotor coil which receives the same a.c. as the rotor coil of the transmitter. The stator coils of the receiver are connected to the corresponding stator coils of the transmitter. If both rotors are in the same angular position, the fields in the corresponding stator coils are equal in strength, generating equal e.m.f.s in them, and no current flows between them. If the rotors are in different

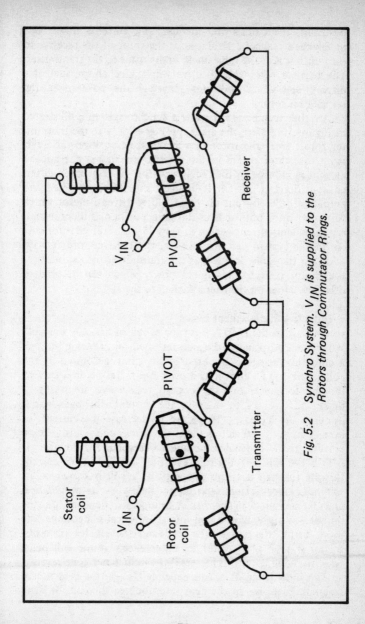

Fig. 5.2 Synchro System. V_{IN} is supplied to the Rotors through Commutator Rings.

positions, the e.m.f.s are unequal, and currents flow. The unbalanced magnetic field causes the rotor of the receiver to turn until it is at the same angle as the rotor of the transmitter. The receiver rotor able to drive a light mechanism, such as a display dial which indicates remotely the position of the transmitter rotor.

Another technique for using a synchro system is illustrated in Figure 5.3. Here the a.c. supply goes only to the transmitter rotor. If the rotors are in the same position the fields from the stator rotors in the receiver are in balance and no current is induced in the receiver stator. If they are in different positions, a current is induced and this is detected and amplified. The output of the amplifier drives a motor which turns the rotor until it is in the same position as the transmitter rotor and current ceases to flow in the receiver rotor coil. As in the system described above, the receiver rotor always takes up the same position as the transmitter rotors, but here the motor provides additional power which can be used to drive any other mechanism attached to the system.

4 Inductive displacement sensor

In contrast to the LVDT, this type of sensor has only one coil. When we try to change the amount of current flowing through a coil, this change is opposed by an e.m.f. generated by the coil. The e.m.f., known as a *back e.m.f.*, results in a current tending to cancel out the current change we are trying to make. If we try to increase the current, the back e.m.f. opposes the increase. If we try to decrease the current, or even switch it off altogether, the back e.m.f. produces a current in the original direction, to keep current flowing. It is as if the coil is trying to prevent any change in the current flowing through it. This property of a coil is known as its *self-inductance*, often referred to simply as its *inductance*, and is measured in *henries*. Inductance depends on the number of turns in the coil and its physical dimensions: the more turns, the longer the coil and the greater its cross-sectional area, the greater its inductance. If the coil has a ferromagnetic core, this increases the inductance considerably.

The inductance of a coil depends also on the presence of magnetic materials in the neighbourhood of the coil. If these

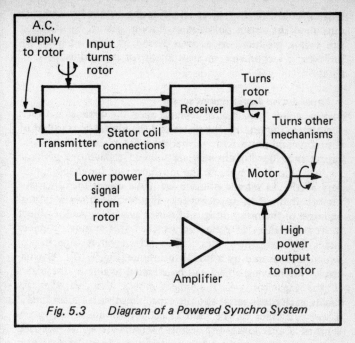

Fig. 5.3   Diagram of a Powered Synchro System

are ferromagnetic, the effect is greatest but paramagnetic and diamagnetic materials also have an effect. A metallic object placed close to the coil alters its inductance, which varies according to the position of the object. To sense the position of the object, we require a circuit sensitive to changes in inductance. One of the simplest ways of building such a circuit is to make the coil part of an oscillator. Changes in the inductance of the coil cause the frequency to change. We then have only to measure the frequency, from which the position of the object can be determined. Measurement of frequency can conveniently be done by a digital circuit. Inductance can also be measured by including the coil in a bridge circuit (page 13).

The principle of self-inductance is sometimes used in proximity sensors. The device is similar to that described above but its output circuit is adapted to change state when a metallic object approaches within a given distance of the sensing coil. If the object is a rotating toothed wheel, the output of the sensor pulses as each tooth passes. By counting the pulses produced in a given period of time we have the basis for a tachometer, an instrument for measuring speed of rotation.

5 Capacitative displacement sensor

In a capacitor, capacitance depends upon the distance between the plates, the area of the plates and the dielectric constant of the non-conductive material between the plates. Changes of capacitance due to distance are used in capacitative pressure sensors (Fig. 4.7) because the movement of the diaphragm is very small. In sensing position we make use of the other two factors that affect capacitance. Figure 5.4 shows a typical example of the many designs of sensor available. As the object moves, the sheet of dielectric attached to the moving object slides between the plates. This action varies capacitance, which is measured by a bridge technique (Fig. 1.10). Alternatively, the moving object can be coupled to one of the plates of the capacitor. As the object moves, the area of plates facing each other varies and the capacitance varies accordingly. These principles can be used to make both linear and rotary sensors. Capacitance displacement sensors are sometimes used as proximity sensors, for example in intruder-detection systems, but they are unreliable.

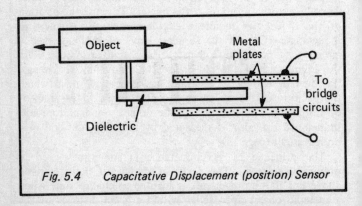

Fig. 5.4   Capacitative Displacement (position) Sensor

6 Optical position sensors

These operate on the principle of illuminating a surface on the moving object and measuring the amount of light being reflected back. The further away the object is positioned the less light is reflected. This technique does not give a linear response but it has the advantage that it operates at a distance and does not exert any force on the object. The same idea is used in proximity detectors. For greater reliability the beam may be pulsed at a fixed frequency, say 1kHz. The sensor incorporates a circuit tuned to respond only to signals at that frequency. This has the advantage that the sensor ignores spurious input from the surroundings and, more than this, is able to pick up and act upon a comparatively weak signal against a background of interference.

7 Encoders

In the simplest type of encoding system the moving object is attached to a strip which is marked with evenly-spaced bars. The bars may be conductive areas on a non-conductive strip, detected by brush contacts, magnetised bars on a non-magnetic strip, or opaque bars on a transparent strip. The latter system is the most popular, since the bars can be detected by having an infra-red LED below the strip and an infra-red photodiode above it (Fig. 5.5).

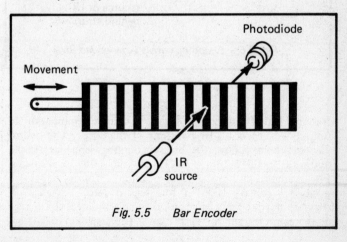

Fig. 5.5   Bar Encoder

This sensing system exerts no frictional force on the strip, and avoids the unreliability of brush contacts and the relative complexity of magnetic sensing circuits. As the object moves, the beam of IR is broken every time a bar passes across it. The processing circuit is digital and counts how many times the beam is broken. The position of the object is known with a precision depending on the spacing of the bars. Such a sensor can register how far the object moves, but not in which direction. By having more than one beam, it is possible for the circuit to determine whether the object is moving to the left or to the right, and thus keep track of its exact position.

A better system is to use a coding pattern such as that in Figure 5.6. This is a binary code with 4 digits. The code is

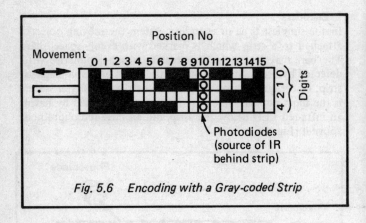

Fig. 5.6   Encoding with a Gray-coded Strip

read by four IR sensors and gives a unique combination of outputs for each of 16 positions of the strip. The coding pattern could follow the binary counting sequence (0000, 0001, 0010, 0011, . . . , 1111), but this leads to problems. For example, in moving from position 7 (binary 0111) to position 8 (binary 1000) all four sensors detect a change. If they are not precisely lined up, they do not detect the change at the same instant for each digit. The sequence might be:

84

Position 7	0111		
Change 2nd digit	0011	3	
Change 4th digit	0010	2	} spurious readings
Change 1st digit	1010	10	
Change 3rd digit	1000		
(= Position 8)			

This gives three spurious readings between positions 7 and 8, and there are similar errors at every other change of position. The solution to this is to let only one digit change at a time, as in Figure 5.6. This system is known as a *Gray code*.

The encoder principle can be applied both to linear position, as above, and to angular position. The project at the end of this chapter uses disc coded with a 3-digit Gray code to sense wind direction. The project illustrates the way in which the Gray code is decoded to convert it to a measure of angular rotation. Encoding methods have the feature that they give rise to a digital signal. This is easily processed by logical circuits. For this reason position encoders are important in robotics and in applications in which computers are involved.

8 Moiré fringe detector

The precision of encoders of the type described previously is limited by the spacing of the bars, which are typically several millimetres across. One way of improving upon this is to make use of moiré fringes. An easy way to demonstrate this phenomenon is to take two identical combs and hold them at a slight angle to each other (Fig. 5.7). The moiré fringe effect is seen as a series of dark and light bands running approximately at right angles to the direction of the teeth of the combs. As you slide one comb horizontally past the other, the fringes move up or down. The point about this operation is that the vertical movement of the fringes is much greater than the horizontal movement of the comb. The effect amplifies the changes in position of the moving comb.

In moiré fringe detectors there are two transparent strips marked with opaque bars. The fixed strip has vertical bars and the moveable strip has bars inclined at a very slight angle to the vertical. Optical sensors detect the moiré fringes and a digital circuit counts them as they move. A slight horizontal

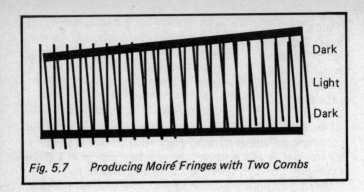

Dark

Light

Dark

Fig. 5.7   *Producing Moiré Fringes with Two Combs*

movement of a strip, less than the spacing between adjacent bars, causes a number of fringes to move vertically, giving the instrument greater precision than the encoder described in Section 6.

9 Position-sensing switches

In many applications it is only necessary to know when the moving object has reached a defined position. We have already mentioned a number of proximity detectors which can be adapted to perform this function. Another frequently used position-sensor is the microswitch. It is used, for example, to detect whether a door is closed or open, or whether a moving part of a machine has reached the end of its permitted range of travel. The term microswitch does not refer to the physical size of the switch mechanism but to the fact that only a very small pressure is needed to actuate the switch. The switch mechanism has a snap action and responds to a small force, often only a few newton. The force must be appreciably reduced before the switch snaps back again. Another position-sensing switch is the Hall-effect switch described on page 119.

10 Attitude sensors

In construction work it is frequently necessary to ensure that buildings or parts of bridges, and other structures are truly vertical. The device traditionally used for this purpose is the plumb line. Other parts of buildings and structures need to be

86

exactly horizontal, for which purpose a spirit level is employed. The electronic equivalent of these instruments may have a pendulum hanging freely from a ball bearing. The position of the bob with reference to the case of the instrument is sensed by using one of the techniques described above, usually by resistive, reluctive or capacitative sensors.

One of the problems of navigating aeroplanes and submarines is knowing exactly where they are and the orientation of the path in which they are travelling. Such vehicles are out of direct contact with the Earth's surface, moving in a fluid medium in three dimensions. The key to fixing their position and attitude depends on establishing a firm frame of reference. A gyroscope is used to provide a stable reference, since a massive wheel spinning at high speed has a considerable degree of directional inertia. The wheel is mounted on gimbals which allow it to turn freely in all directions. Once the gyro has been set, and brought up to full speed, its axis remains pointing in the same direction, whatever direction the vehicle turns in. Sensors on the gimbals detect the motion of the axis relative to the frame of the aeroplane or submarine. From this information, together with information about the vehicle's speed, it is possible to compute the current position with reference to Earth.

Satellites and spacecraft make use of telescopic sensors that locate the bearings of celestial objects such as the Sun or one or more of the brighter stars. If the craft is close to a planet, the sensor may instead detect the edge between the sunlit and dark side of the planet and use this for reference. A computer is required to carry out the complex calculations, using the data from the sensors to arrive at the location and attitude of the craft. A more sophisticated technique is to use a charge-coupled device to detect a number of the brighter stars. The CCD has a target screen on which an image of the sky is focussed. Even at extremely low levels, the light arriving from each star causes a charge to accumulate on the corresponding point on the screen. An electron beam scans the screen in a regular raster (similar to that on a TV screen). The output of the device alters whenever the beam encounters a charged point. The information from the CCD is processed and compared with star patterns stored in the computer. By this means the stars are identified automatically and the attitude of the spacecraft determined.

PROJECT 5 – Wind Direction Indicator (Level 2)

This project comprises a wind vane to detect the direction of the wind and an LED display conveniently situated indoors. The display is an 8-point compass, with an LED at each point to indicate current wind direction.

How It Works

The wind vane (Fig. 5.8) is of a conventional pattern, mounted outdoors as high as possible and as far as possible from buildings and trees, where it is exposed to the wind in all directions. The box on which the vane is mounted houses the circuit which codes wind direction into one of 8 Gray codes. The shaft of the vane has a circular transparent disc on it, with sectors painted black, as in Figure 5.9. The three concentric rings of sectors range from the digit 0 on the outside, to digit 2 on the inside. A row of 3 light-emitting diodes above the disc are the IR sources, and their radiation is detected by a row of 3 IR photodiodes below (Fig. 5.10). Each photodiode is in

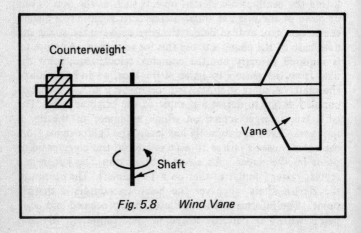

Fig. 5.8   Wind Vane

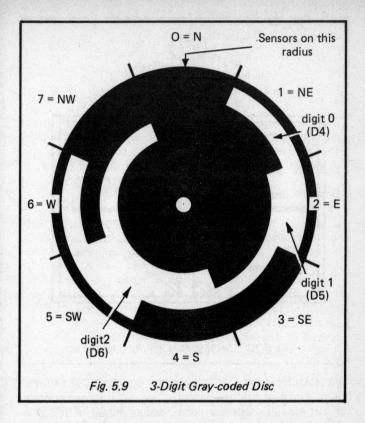

Fig. 5.9 *3-Digit Gray-coded Disc*

series with a 470kΩ resistor (Fig. 5.11). For simplicity, only one of the diode pairs is shown in the figure.

When the photodiode is receiving IR, the increased leakage current flowing through the resistor causes a p.d. across it. This acts as a logical high input to the NAND gate. Since both inputs to the NAND gate are connected, the gate behaves as a NOT gate. Its output goes low. When the disc sector between the LED and photodiode is black, the gate output goes high.

The encoder box is connected to the main instrument case by a 5-wire cable; 2 supply lines plus one for each digit. The 3 inputs from the encoder are decoded by a pair of exclusive-OR gates to give a true 3-digit binary output. This is fed to

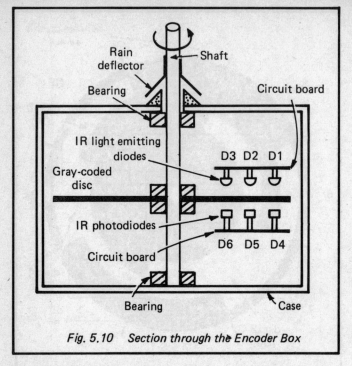

Fig. 5.10   Section through the Encoder Box

the select inputs of a BCD-to-decimal decoder (IC3) with the fourth (D) digit held permanently low. At any given position of the encoding disc the corresponding output of IC3 goes high, the others remaining low. The outputs from IC3 go to a non-inverting buffer, to provide sufficient power to light an LED on the display panel (Fig. 5.12). For simplicity, only one of the display LEDs is shown in Figure 5.11.

Construction

The details of construction of the wind vane are left to the reader, as they depend upon materials and tools available. The main requirements are that it should be light yet robust, and able to turn freely in the wind. It is fairly easy to adapt a ready-made vane for this project, or a local engineer could make one at relatively low cost.

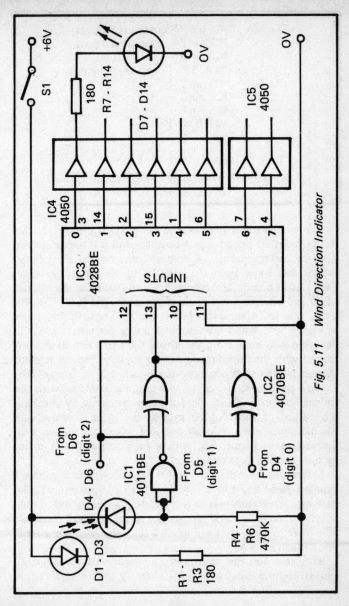

Fig. 5.11   Wind Direction Indicator

```
To +6V:   IC1 pin 14 and unused inputs
          IC2 pin 14 and unused inputs
          IC3 pin 16
          IC 4, 5 Pin 1 and unused inputs
To OV:    IC1 pin 7
          IC2 pin 7
          IC3 pin 8
          IC4, 5 pin 8
```

Fig. 5.11   Wind Direction Indicator (continued)

The encoder box need not be perfectly light-proof, as the photodiodes are close to the IR sources, but it is important for it to be weatherproof. A conical collar on the shaft helps deflect rain away from the aperture in the top of the box. Two circuit-boards are required, a small one for the source LEDs and a larger one for the photodiodes and IC1. The disc is cut from stiff transparent plastic and painted with the design of Figure 5.9. When the vane is pointing due north, i.e. as if the wind is coming from the north, the LEDs and diodes are aligned with the radius marked in the figure. Thus the reading changes to NE or NW when the disc is turned 22½° from north.

Wire up the encoder circuit and install it in its case with the enoder disc on its shaft. Test the encoder circuit by checking the output of each NAND gate as the shaft is turned one complete revolution. Voltages should follow the sequence of the sectors in Figure 5.9, with a high output (+6V) corresponding with a clear sector.

Mount the encoder box with vane attached in a suitably exposed place and run a cable down to the instrument case indoors. Preferably use 5-way light-duty cable, but 6-way telephone cable is suitable. As the signal is digital there are no problems with voltage loss and the cable may be several tens of metres long.

The case for the main circuit board needs to be large enough to hold the circuit and the battery, and to have a front

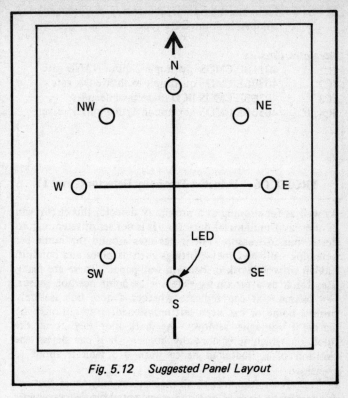

Fig. 5.12   Suggested Panel Layout

panel large enough for the display. The switch S1 is mounted on the front panel. The switch could be a push-button, so that power is used and the wind direction displayed only when the button is pressed. If this system is adopted, a 6V battery of 4AA cells will last for years.

Details of Special Parts

Semiconductors

D1—D3   IR light-emitting diode; a small 3mm miniature diode is sufficient, with light output 3.5mW at 40mA

D4—D6   Photodiode, general purpose type, preferably in a TO18 case with an end window.

D7–D14   Light-emitting diode, red or any preferred colour/
           colours, high-intensity type.

Integrated Circuits
IC1   4011BE CMOS quadruple 2-input NAND gate
IC2   4070BE CMOS quadruple exclusive-OR gate
IC3   4028BE CMOS BCD-to-decimal decoder
IC4, IC5   4050BE CMOS hex non-inverting buffer/driver.

PROJECT 6 – Inductive Proximity Detector (Level 1)

As well as functioning as a proximity detector this circuit can
be used as a mini-metal detector. It is not sensitive enough to
detect buried treasure, but it has uses around the home for
detecting nails and metal fittings such as pipes and conduit,
hidden in woodwork or beneath wall-paper. There are many
uses for it as a proximity detector or point position sensor.
For example, it can indicate whether a door bolt is safely
pushed home or has been left unfastened, or it can raise the
alarm if someone removes the back-door key from the
hook on which it is normally hung. Or it can detect the
position of a float and hence warn if a tank is about to
overflow.

The sensor responds to all metals, not only those that are
ferromagnetic such as iron and steel, but also to paramagnetic
and diamagnetic metals, such as aluminium, copper, silver and
lead, and to alloys such as cupro-nickel (coins), brass, and
solder. The range of the sensor is up to about 20mm from
the end of the search coil.

How It Works
The sensor element is a search coil of enamelled copper wire
wound on a ferrite core (Fig. 5.13). This is wired in parallel
with a capacitor (C1, Fig. 5.14) as part of a circuit oscillating
at about 300kHz. The amplitude of the oscillations is high
when there is no metal in the region of the coil, since the
oscillator produces waves with strong crests and peaks. The

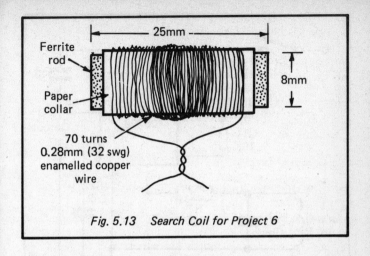

Fig. 5.13   Search Coil for Project 6

presence of a metal object close to the coil alters the magnetic field in this region, interfering with the operation of the oscillator. It reduces the Q of the circuit. The result is a marked decrease in the amplitude of the oscillations. Circuits in the IC detect the drop in amplitude by comparing it with a reference. The result is a change in output level at pins 4 and 5. The output of pin 4 is high when amplitude is high but swings sharply low as amplitude begins to fall. The output of pin 5 changes in the opposite sense.

There are various ways in which the output can be used. Figure 5.14(a) shows how to wire an LED to pin 4 of IC1, so that the LED is normally out, but comes on when metal is detected. If connected to pin 5 instead of pin 4, the LED goes out when the metal is near. With a red LED connected to pin 4 and a green one connected to pin 5, the green LED glows when there is no metal near, and the red one glows when metal is detected. Other devices can be connected instead of, or in parallel with, the LED in Figure 5.14(a). An obvious choice is a solid-state buzzer or audible warning device, so that the detector gives audible indication as well as visual indication that metal is near. Another possible device is a relay coil, the contacts of which could be wired into a home security system.

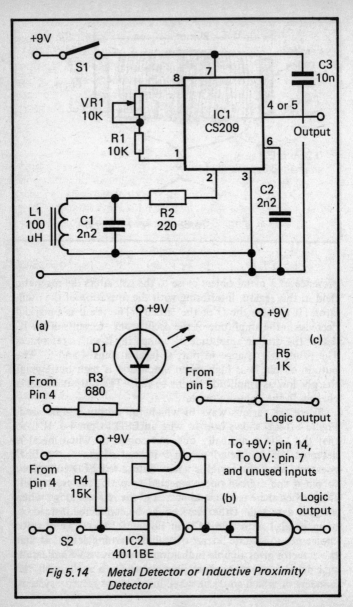

Fig 5.14   Metal Detector or Inductive Proximity
Detector

Usually the LED is to be lit only when metal is near but, if it is required for the presence of metal to trigger the circuit permanently, connect a flip-flop to pin 4, as in Figure 5.14(b). The output from pin 4 acts as a logic high, setting the flip-flop when it goes low. This causes a high output to appear at the third gate. The flip-flop is reset by pressing S2. Pin 5 can also supply a logical output but requires a pull-up resistor, as in Figure 5.14(c).

Construction

The probe coil can be purchased ready-made as a $100\mu H$ choke. Alternatively, wind the coil on a length of ferrite rod sawn from a ferrite aerial rod. First wrap a rectangle of paper around the rod and secure it with self-adhesive tape. Then wind the coil of about 70 turns; it need not be wound regularly. Twist the wires together a few times where they emerge from the coil and scrape the enamel from their ends.

The circuit is small and runs on a 9V PP3 battery. It would be convenient to house the circuit in a 'calculator-type' plastic case, with an integral battery compartment. The search coil could be mounted in the front end of the case, with one end of the search coil flush with the front, or just protruding.

When laying out the strip-board or PCB, keep all connections as short as possible, especially those to the search coil and C1. VR1 provides a sensitivity adjustment but, once this is set, it is not likely that you will need to alter it. A carbon potentiometer ('volume control') can be used, though it is easier to set up the circuit if a multiturn cermet preset resistor is used.

In the test routine which follows we assume that pin 4 is connected to an LED D1, as in Figure 5.12(a). Remove all metal objects from the vicinity of the search coil and switch on. D1 is on when VR1 is turned to give maximum resistance, and goes out as the resistance of VR1 is decreased. Turn VR1 to bring D1 on, then turn it slowly until D1 just goes out. Bring a metal object close to the coil; D1 comes on. If D1 stays on when the object is removed again, turn VR1 a small distance back again, until D1 goes on and off as the metal is brought near and then removed.

Details of Special Parts

Capacitors
C1, C2   2n2 polystyrene
C3   10n polyester or ceramic disc

Integrated Circuits
IC1   CS209 electro-magnetic proximity detector
IC2   4011BE CMOS quadruple 2-input NAND gate (optional).

Chapter 6

SOUND SENSORS

Sound consists of vibrations of the air or other medium at frequencies which we can hear. It is difficult to define the exact frequency at which a series of individual pulses becomes a continuous low-pitched hum but, for practical purposes, we can take 30Hz as the lowest frequency that is considered to be sound. At the other extreme, the upper limit of hearing varies with individuals. A frequency of about 20kHz is a reasonable figure to take. Above this range there is ultra-sound, not detectable by the human ear, though many other animals such as cats and dogs are sensitive to it. In particular, the frequency of 40kHz is a common one selected for use with devices which operate by ultra-sound.

Sound sensors are more often known as *microphones*. There are several different types, described in outline below. Some are designed for use with audio systems, others are intended for precision measurement of sound level in acoustic studies and industrial applications. Whatever field the microphone is intended for, the same general principles of construction and operation apply.

Measurements of sound are usually expressed as *sound pressure level*, in decibels. The SPL is given by:

$$\text{SPL} = 20 \log_{10} \frac{p}{p_{ref}}$$

where p is the root mean square of the effective pressure produced by the sound over a specified period of time, and p_{ref} is the root mean square of a reference pressure. The reference pressure is usually specified as 2×10^{-4} μbar, equivalent to 2×10^{-5} Pa. The sensitivity of a microphone is quoted in decibels as $20 \log_{10}(V/p)$, where V is the root mean square output in volts and p is the effective pressure of the sound.

The *sound level*, often used as a measure of loudness, is the sound pressure level over the entire audible range, usually weighted according to the response of a typical human ear. There are three common weightings used in sound level meters: weighting A has the extreme frequencies reduced in power, by −11dB at 100Hz and by a similar amount at 10kHz; weighting B is reduced by about −4dB at 100Hz and 10kHz; weighting C is the unweighted sound level.

1 Carbon granule microphone

This consists of a container loosely filled with carbon granules (Fig. 6.1). The front of the container is a thin metal diaphragm and at its rear is a metal plate or electrode. The microphone requires an external power supply, which is connected across the diaphragm and the rear electrode. The carbon granules provide a conduction path, the resistance of the path varying with the pressure of the diaphragm on them, and the pressure of the granules on each other, as they are vibrated by sound. Thus the output signal is a current, varying with the form of the sound waves.

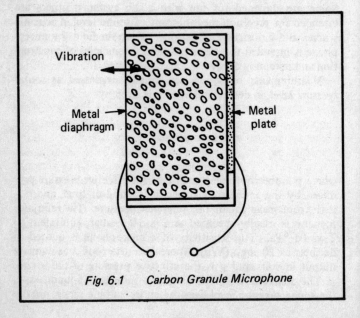

Fig. 6.1   Carbon Granule Microphone

Carbon microphones are robust and inexpensive and were widely used in telephones. They have the advantage that the output signal is large and needs little amplification. But such a microphone is subject to resonance. That is to say, there are certain frequencies at which the response of the microphone is particularly high. The output of the microphone is thus a distorted replica of the original sound. This may not matter with a speech signal, but reproduction of music is extremely poor. There is also the problem of excessive *noise*, random variations in the signal brought about as the carbon granules move against each other.

2 Electromagnetic microphones

There are two forms of these, moving-iron and moving-coil. In the moving-iron microphone (Fig. 6.2(a)) the magnetic field is provided by a strong permanent magnet, which acts as a core to the pick-up coil. The diaphragm is a thin metal sheet, which vibrates with sound. This causes fluctuations in the magnetic field within the coil and generates a fluctuating e.m.f. across the coil, a fairly good replica of the original sound waves. The current resulting from the e.m.f. is reasonably large so little amplification is required. The main disadvantage of this type is that it is weighty. Another problem is that the coil readily responds to the alternating magnetic field from any nearby mains-powered equipment, imposing a 50Hz 'hum' on its output.

The moving-coil (dynamic) microphone of Figure 6.2(b) is less subject to hum, is more compact, and has much better linearity. Sound vibrations cause the coil to move within the magnetic field of the permanent magnet, inducing a fluctuating e.m.f. in it. It gives a reasonably strong output signal. As already mentioned, resonance is a problem in the design of most types of microphone. One part or another is likely to resonate at one or more frequencies. One solution to the problem is to damp out resonance by packing the microphone with elastic material to absorb the vibration. This approach often leads to further difficulties. A better solution is to reduce the mass of the resonating part, so that it resonates at a higher frequency, above 30kHz. Its resonance then becomes inaudible.

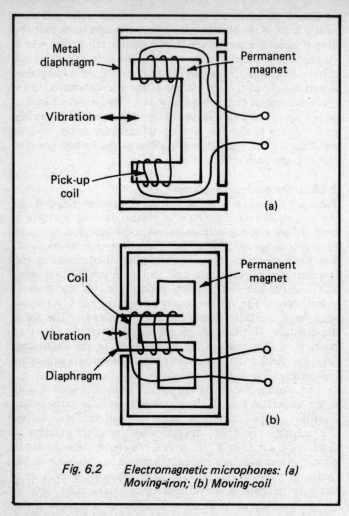

Fig. 6.2 *Electromagnetic microphones: (a) Moving-iron; (b) Moving-coil*

3 Piezo-electric microphone

The quartz crystal microphone is one of the most frequently-used microphones. Vibrations of the diaphragm are transmitted to a piezo-electric crystal, generating an e.m.f. (Fig. 6.3). The e.m.f. is smaller than that produced by the

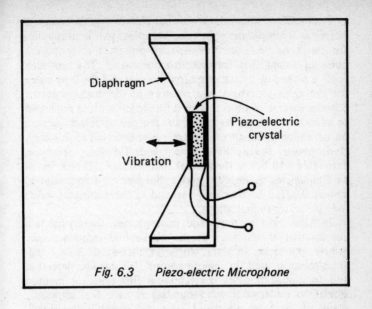

Fig. 6.3   Piezo-electric Microphone

microphones already described and the crystal has high output impedance. That is to say, it is not able to supply a large current to an amplifier without loss of voltage. The output signal is liable to be lost or at least degraded if the microphone is connected to the amplifying equipment by a cable of anything more than minimal length. If a longer run of cable is essential, a pre-amplifier with FET (i.e. high impedance) input is located in the microphone case. This produces a more robust signal that passes unharmed along a cable, and may not need further amplification.

However, amplification introduces the possibility of the microphone picking up mains hum unless care is taken to shield it and the cable. There is also the disadvantage that the amplifier requires a battery to supply it with power, making the microphone bulky, or it must be supplied with power from external equipment. Instead of a quartz crystal, a ceramic piezo-electric material may be used, and has a better frequency response. However, the response of piezo-electric microphones is not as good as that of the magnetic types.

Piezo-electric microphones are suitable for operation under water, as *hydrophones*. In echo-sounding, two hydrophones are used; one being used as a sound generator to produce a pulse of sound that radiates into the water. The returning echo is picked up by the other hydrophone and the time taken for the echo to return is a measure of the distance of the echoing surface or object. This information is often processed so as to give a visual display of the sea bed or objects located on or above it. Shoals of fish are easily detected in this way. Hydrophones usually have a very wide frequency response, extending well below the normal audible range. They respond to frequencies as high as 16kHz, but also to frequencies as low as 0.03Hz, so that they respond to the passing of waves over the water-surface above.

In ultra-sonic piezo-electric microphones, the crystal is a cut so that it resonates at the ultra-sound frequency, say 40kHz, generating an e.m.f. whenever ultra-sound is detected. Ultra-sound is used for remote control, for intruder detection and for applications of the echo-sounding type. A method similar to underwater echo-sounding is used for 'ultrasonic scans' of the human body. Ultra-sound is highly directional. Beams of ultra-sound, concentrated by acoustic lenses, can be projected into the body and are reflected back whenever they meet a discontinuity in the tissues. With complex processing circuits we display the outline of an unborn infant in the uterus, or the contours of the brain. A similar technique is used for detecting welding flaws in metal structures.

4 Capacitor microphone

Capacitor microphones work like most other capacitative sensors (e.g. Fig. 4.7) by sensing the change in capacitance between a vibrating metal or metallised plastic diaphragm and a fixed plate. An external source of polarising potential is required. A relative of this microphone is the *electret* microphone. In this, a dielectric material between two metal plates is heated during manufacture and then cooled while in a strong electric field. This causes a permanent electric field to be held in the dielectric. Vibration of the electret causes an e.m.f. to be generated between the plates. With both types of capacitative microphone, signal level is low and output impedance is high. An amplifier with battery supply is often included in the microphone case. The quality of sound produced by this type of microphone is very high.

5 Ribbon microphone

As shown in Figure 6.4 this consists of a light metallic ribbon suspended between the poles of a permanent magnet. Movement of the ribbon caused by sound results in an e.m.f. being induced in the ribbon. Since there is only the ribbon, not a long coiled wire, the output of this microphone is low and a built-in amplifier is required. The quality of sound is very

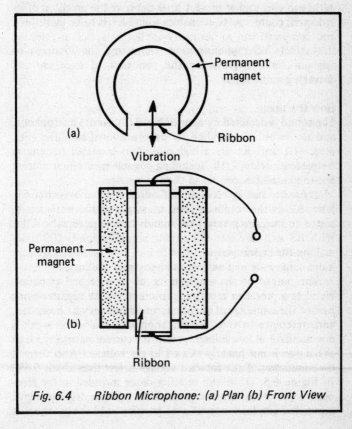

Fig. 6.4   *Ribbon Microphone: (a) Plan (b) Front View*

good and it also has the property of being very directional. That is to say, it is especially sensitive to sounds arriving along the axis of the microphone. This makes it particularly useful in a high-noise environment. It does not pick up mains hum readily. The manufacture of a ribbon microphone has to be very precise and consequently it is very expensive.

PROJECT 7 – Sound Level Meter (Level 1)

Although this simple project does not have the precision of its industrial counterparts, it enables sound levels to be monitored and compared and so has many applications such as assessing the effects of sound-proofing, estimating the loudness of applause, and investigating the incidence of excessive and damaging sound levels.

How It Works
The sound is detected by a moving-coil (dynamic) microphone, and its output is amplified by an operational amplifier (Fig. 6.5). C1 and R1 are a high-pass filter intended to remove frequencies below 72Hz, including possible mains interference, but to pass all frequencies in the audio range.

There are two levels of amplification selected by switch S2. With R2 as the feedback resistor, amplification is 10 times, suited to measuring very loud sounds such as pneumatic drills. With R3 switched into the circuit, amplification is 100 times making the instrument sensitive to low-level sounds such as are more commonly met with in domestic surroundings.

The output of the amplifier is fed to a second amplifier, wired as a precision rectifier. This removes the negative-going part of the sound signal so that its amplitude may be measured, with reference to 0V. Rectification with a diode network is not accurate at low voltages, when the current passing through the diode is not linearly related to the voltage. Also there is no conduction if the forward voltage is less than about 0.6V. In Figure 6.5, D1 is the rectifier diode included in the feed-back loop of the inverting amplifier. For a negative signal input, the amplifier output goes positive until the potential at

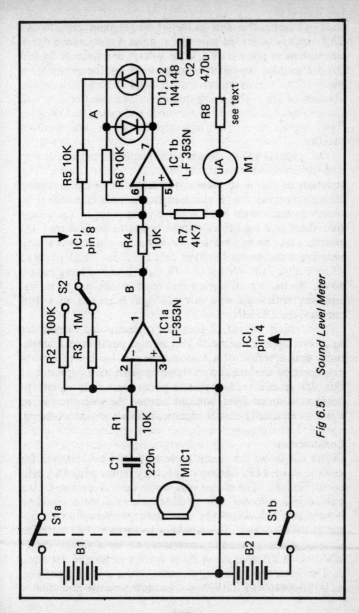

Fig 6.5   Sound Level Meter

the (−) input is the same as that at the (+) input, close to 0V. This happens when the potential at point A is equal and opposite to that at point B (V_{IN}), the voltage drops across R4 and R6 being equal. In order to bring this about, the output from pin 7 of IC1b rises higher than it would normally do in the absence of D1. This compensates for the non-linearity and the forward voltage drop of the diode and means that negative input signals of a few millivolts amplitude are rectified precisely.

On positive-going signals, the amplifier output swings negative, and the potential at point A remains at zero. The function of D2 is to prevent the amplifier output swinging strongly negative for, if this occurs, the time taken for it to return to zero on the next negative-going swing of V_{IN} means that there is a lag before output begins to go positive. D2 ensures that the (−) reaches 0V when the output has swung only twice the forward voltage drop (to about −1.2V) instead of all the way to −6V (or to −9V if the circuit is being run on ±9V). To make rectification even more precise an operational amplifier with high slew rate (13V/μs) is chosen, in a dual package, the LF353N.

The output from IC1b goes to a capacitor and charges this to a level approximating to the average positive peak amplitude, over a period of a few seconds. It has been found in practice that the amount of damping given by a capacitor of this size gives a reading that responds reasonably closely to changes in sound level, without causing the meter needle to move so erratically that it becomes difficult to take a reading.

Construction
Figure 6.5 shows the circuit powered by two 6V batteries, for each of which a PP1 battery or a battery holder with 4AA cells could be used. The circuit also works on ±9V provided by a pair of PP3 batteries. A portable hand-held meter could be housed in a 'calculator-type' case, with the microphone mounted at the front end. This would be powered by PP3 batteries. On the whole it is more convenient to use a slightly larger case, which provides more room for the meter and batteries.

The prototype was constructed for a microphone with −80dB sensitivity (70μV/bar). If a more sensitive microphone is used, it may be necessary to reduce the value of R2 and R3.

A moving-coil meter is preferred to a digital panel meter as the swinging of the needle gives a much better impression of the variations of sound level than do the rapidly changing figures of a digital display. The meter consists of a milli-ammeter in series with a resistor R8 to give full-scale deflection when the output of IC1b is at its maximum. This depends on the power supply voltage. On a ±6V supply, the maximum output is about 4.5V. On a ±9V supply it is about 7V. The value of R8 is calculated as:

$$\frac{\text{f.s. voltage}}{\text{f.s. current}} - r$$

where 'f.s. voltage' is 4.5V or 7V (depending on whether the supply is ±6V or ±9V), 'f.s. current' is the full scale current of the meter and r is the resistance of the meter coil. Thus a 100μA meter with coil resistance 3750Ω, operating with a ±6V supply requires a resistor

$$4.5/(100 \times 10^{-6}) - 3750 = 41250\Omega$$

The next largest standard resistor, 43kΩ, is used.

Calibration

If you prefer, read the sound level in arbitrary units, simply by taking the reading direct from the meter scale. This is all that is required if measurements are being taken for the purpose of comparison. Alternatively the meter can be roughly calibrated in decibels against various sources of sound. If possible, the microphone is held 1 metre from the sound source. Sources can include whispering (10dB), ordinary conversation (50dB), a motor horn (80dB), jet-plane taking off (100dB). Some of these sources are very variable, so you may need to average out several results to obtain a reasonable calibration. The sound levels of sirens and buzzers such as those used in security systems (and in some of the projects in this book) are usually quoted in the catalogues, so these make reasonably good sources for calibrating the meter.

Details of Special Parts

Integrated Circuits
IC1   LF353N dual FET-input operational amplifier.

Miscellaneous
MIC1   The prototype had a dynamic microphone, sensitive in the range 100Hz to 10kHz.

PROJECT 8 – Sound-controlled Switch (Levels 1–3)

The switch is operated by any whistling sound of the correct pitch. It has many applications as a remote control switch including turning on and off a radio set, a tape recorder or a table lamp. It has a range of several metres and is capable of operating in a noisy environment since the circuit responds only to its tuned frequency, even though sounds of other frequencies are being detected simultaneously.

This project has a considerable 'fun-appeal' as a novel way of switching, but it has its serious applications too. It could be an invaluable aid to an handicapped or elderly person. Model railway enthusiasts might adapt it for controlling their locomotives more realistically, by blowing a whistle.

The circuit responds almost instantly to sounds in the frequency range 1.2kHz to 1.8kHz. It has a toggle action, turning on the first time it is whistled at and turning off the next time. An LED indicates whether the switch is on or off. An optional addition to the circuit is an 'answer-back' bleeper which emits a 2-second bleep every time the switch is turned on. This gives audible indication of the circuit state, helpful if the whistler is not able to see the LED. As set out in Figure 6.6, with the relay switching battery-powered devices, this is a beginners' project. With the addition of the bleeper it becomes a Level 2 project. If the switch is used to control mains-powered equipment it definitely becomes a Level 3

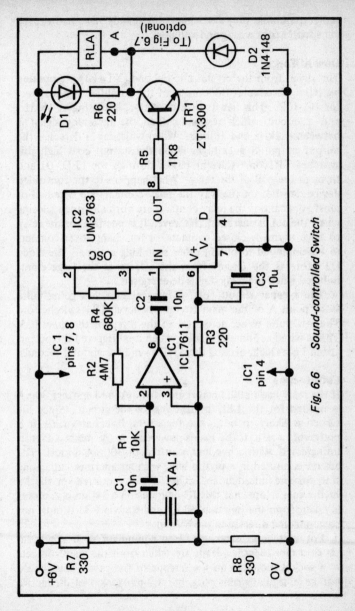

Fig. 6.6   Sound-controlled Switch

111

project, suitable only for those who already have had experience with mains wiring and voltages.

How It Works

The signal from the crystal microphone (XTAL1) is amplified by IC1. C2 couples the output of the amplifier to the detector IC, IC2. This has its own oscillator, operating at 18kHz, and a circuit which responds when the incoming signal is between 1.2kHz and 1.8kHz. When whistling is detected the output at pin 8 goes high. When the output goes high this switches TR1 on. Current passes through the LED, D1 and through the coil of the relay. What happens to the controlled device depends on the way the relay contacts are wired. For most applications the relay contacts are normally open, closing when the coil is energised. However, it is possible for the relay to have normally-closed contacts, or for change-over contacts to be employed to obtain other switching actions. The diode D2 protects the circuit from the effects of the large e.m.f. induced when the relay coil is de-energised.

The bleeper circuit (Fig. 6.7) receives a low-going pulse from point A of the main circuit whenever TR1 switches on. The low pulse passes across C4 to the input of the timer IC3. This is wired as an monostable. When it is triggered the output at pin 3 goes high, making the AWD sound for about 2 seconds.

Construction

If the relay has a 200Ω coil it draws 30mA, and another 30mA is needed for the LED and the rest of the circuit. Since the switch is likely to be in use for several hours at a time, it is preferable for it to be mains-powered. A 6V mains adaptor, unregulated, with a maximum output of 300mA is ideal. The circuit is housed in a plastic box, with an aperture cut in one side for the microphone. The LED is mounted on the lid of the case. Note that this IC operates on a 3V supply; power is taken from the junction of R7 and R8, via R3. It must not be connected directly to the 6V rail.

For switching battery-powered equipment such as a radio set or a tape-recorder, leads are taken from the relay contacts to a socket mounted on the outside of the case. This should *not* be a regular mains plug, but a 2-pin socket of distinctive

112

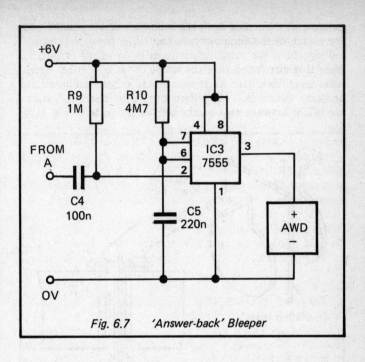

Fig. 6.7   'Answer-back' Bleeper

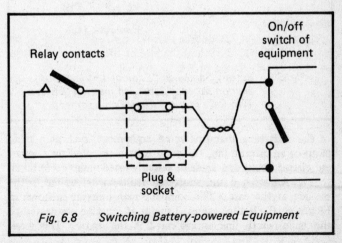

Fig. 6.8   Switching Battery-powered Equipment

pattern. A 2-pin plug to fit the socket is wired in parallel with the switch of the equipment, so that either the sound-controlled switch or the usual switch turns it on or off (Fig. 6.8). Note that interfering with the wiring of radio or other equipment may invalidate its guarantee and other warranties and servicing contracts. An alternative is to insert a 'battery sandwich' between two of the cells in the battery (Fig. 6.9).

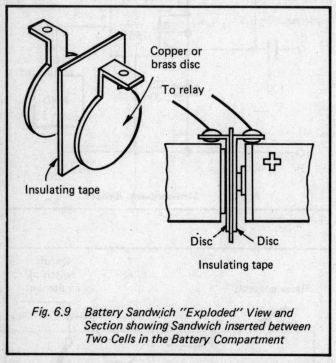

Fig. 6.9   Battery Sandwich "Exploded" View and
Section showing Sandwich inserted between
Two Cells in the Battery Compartment

For switching mains-powered equipment, such as a table lamp or an electric fan, the relay is best mounted on a separate circuit board and leads of suitably rated mains cable taken to a 13A switched and shuttered mains socket bolted to the outside of the case. The complete mains circuit is shown in Figure 6.10. If the case is of metal, it must be connected to the mains earth line as indicated in the figure. **This work**

114

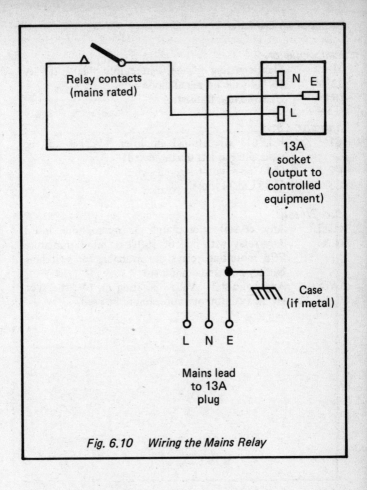

Relay contacts (mains rated)

N E

L

13A socket (output to controlled equipment)

Case (if metal)

L N E

Mains lead to 13A plug

Fig. 6.10   Wiring the Mains Relay

should be undertaken with great care and only by suitably experienced persons.

When testing and using this circuit, remember that it responds to only a narrow range of frequencies. Whistle with a rising or falling pitch, so as to sweep across the sensitive range of the circuit.

Details of Special Parts

Semiconductors
D1   Light-emitting diode, preferably high-intensity
D2   1N4148 silicon signal diode
TR1   ZTX300 npn transistor

Integrated Circuits
IC1   ICL7611 operational amplifier (CA3140 can be
            used, pin 8 is left unconnected)
IC2   UM3763 sound-triggered switch
IC3   7555 CMOS timer

Miscellaneous
XTAL1   Any crystal microphone or microphone insert
RLA   Any relay with coil of 100Ω or more; miniature
            PCB mounting relays are available for switching
            battery-powered equipment
AWD   Any solid-state AWD operating on 6V; the type
            giving a continuous note should be used.

Chapter 7

MAGNETIC SENSORS

One of the most basic ways of measuring a magnetic field is to spin a coil in the field and measure the e.m.f. induced in the coil. This is the principle of the *fluxmeter*. A similar technique is used with the *inductor probe*, which has a stationary coil and measures the strength of an alternating magnetic field. Another instrument relies on *nuclear magnetic resonance* (NMR). Certain substances absorb radiation at radio-frequencies because their nuclei resonate at that frequency. The exact frequency depends linearly on the strength of the local magnetic field. By measuring the absorption frequency we can calculate the strength of the magnetic field. The NMR sensor consists of a capsule containing the substance (for example hydrogen) and a radio-frequency coil. A radio-frequency generator automatically sweeps through a range of radio frequencies and the frequency at which absorption occurs is measured. This technique depends on measuring frequency, a quantity that can be determined with high precision, so we have here a method for measuring magnetic field strength with a precision of 1 part in a million.

Apart from these specialised instruments, the most frequently used magnetic sensors are those which depend on the *Hall effect*, and on the *magnetoresistive effect*. We deal with these in detail below.

1 Hall effect sensors

The Hall effect is the result of the force acting on charged particles as they move in a magnetic field. The particles obey Fleming's Left Hand Rule, the one that applies to electric motors, as shown in Figure 7.1. In Hall effect devices the charged particles are electrons moving through a slice of semiconductor material. The effect also occurs when electrons flow through metal, but is not as strong. In a semiconductor, the result of the deflection of the electrons is that one side of the slice has a higher concentration of electrons than the other; it is more negatively charged than the other. A p.d.

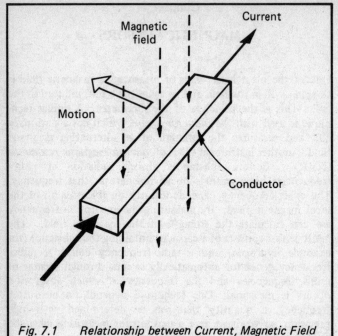

Fig. 7.1   *Relationship between Current, Magnetic Field and the force produced on a Moving Positively Charged Carrier*

is generated across the slice (Fig. 7.2).

Hall effect devices consist of the semiconductor slice with circuits on the same chip for detecting the p.d. and producing an output suited to a particular function. Different devices have different types of output, as the following examples show:

TL170C — operates as an on–off switch, sensitive to field direction; it requires a field of 25mT to turn it on and a reverse field of −25mT to turn it off.

TL172C — operates as a normally-off switch, sensitive to field strength; it is turned on when the magnetic field exceeds 45mT and turns off when the field falls below 22mT.

634SS2 — the voltage output is linearly proportional to field strength and direction in the range −40mT to +40mT.

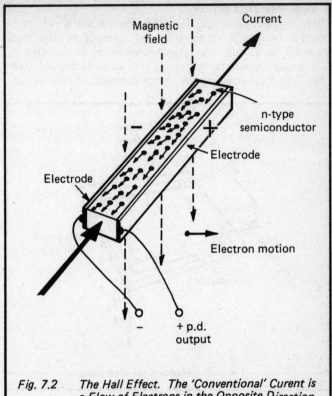

Fig. 7.2 *The Hall Effect. The 'Conventional' Curent is a Flow of Electrons in the Opposite Direction in n-type Semiconductor*

The first two have applications as proximity switches and as position switches. Because there is a clean transition from on to off, the devices are also used for contactless, bounce-free switching. This property is made use of for pressure-sensing in certain types of keyboard switch and micro-switch. When the key-top or plunger is pressed, a tiny magnet inside the switch is brought toward a Hall-effect device. Switching is bounce-free and there are no problems with contact wear. The third device listed above has many applications in the quantitative measurement of magnetic fields.

2 Magnetoresistive devices

These depend upon the fact that the resistivity of ferro-magnetic materials varies with the strength of the local magnetic field. In the magnetoresistive sensor, a strip of ferromagnetic material is deposited on an insulating substrate (Fig. 7.3). Current is supplied from a constant-current circuit.

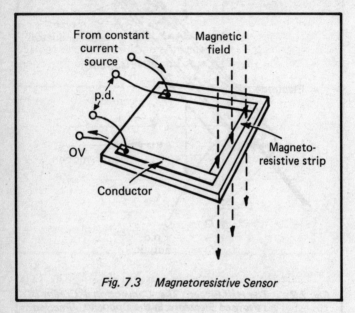

Fig. 7.3   Magnetoresistive Sensor

As the magnetic field varies, variations in the resistivity of the stripe cause measurable variations in the p.d. across the stripe. The effect is not linear but, by various means, such as including a small permanent magnet in the sensor, the device can be biassed to operate linearly over a prescribed range.

Whereas inductive magnetic sensors respond to the *rate of change* of field strength, the magnetoresistive effect (like the Hall effect) depends solely on the field strength at any given time and place. Magnetoresistive devices are widely used as sensors for reading data recorded magnetically on tapes and computer discs. They are also used for reading data on bank cards, credit cards, tickets and identity cards. Because they are unaffected by the rate of change of field strength they are ideal for use in equipment in which magnetic stripes are read while wiped manually past the reading head. They are also used as position and velocity sensors.

3 Reed switches

A reed switch consists of two springy metal contacts sealed in a capsule (Fig. 7.4). In a magnetic field, the contacts become temporarily magnetised. Since the north pole of one contact is close to the south pole of the other, magnetic attraction

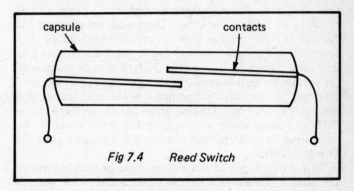

Fig 7.4   Reed Switch

bends the contacts, bringing them together. When the field is removed, they become demagnetised and spring apart. Reed switches are used in reed relays, in which the magnetic field is provided by the energising coil. Their advantage is that their closing time is only 1 or 2 milliseconds, about one-tenth the operating time of electromagnetic relays. Reed switches are also used as position sensors, a typical application being to detect open doors and windows in security systems. The reed switch is mounted on or in the jamb of the door frame and a magnet is mounted on or in the edge of the door itself. As long as the door is closed, the magnet is adjacent to the reed switch, and its contacts are held together magnetically. If the door is opened, the magnet is no longer close to the switch and the contacts spring apart, breaking the security circuit.

PROJECT 9 – Tachometer (Levels 1–2)

A tachometer is a device for measuring the rate of revolution of a wheel or shaft. Various forms of tachometer are described in Chapter 9, but the project is included in this chapter because a magnetic sensor is used. The electronics of this tachometer are simple, so that it is a Level 1 project but, depending on what application you choose, you may require a certain amount of mechanical skill to install it.

One way of using the tachometer is for measuring the rate of revolution of an anemometer, or wind speed meter. This is either a propellor mounted on a vane to keep it pointing into the wind, or a rotor with three hemispherical or conical cups revolving on a vertical spindle. The mechanical parts are not difficult to build and can also be purchased ready-made. The spindle of the propellor or rotor has a plastic disc mounted on it, with a magnet on its rim (Fig. 7.5). For every rotation of the spindle the magnet passes the sensor and a pulse is generated. The rate of rotation is proportional to the wind speed. The anemometer must be calibrated, either against another already-calibrated anemometer exposed to the same winds, or by comparing its readings with wind speeds estimated using the Beaufort Scale.

In a similar way, the tachometer could be used to measure the rate of rotation of a bicycle wheel and thus the speed at which the bicycle is going. There are numerous other uses for it, for measuring the speed of rotation of a drill, or of any other machinery or engine and for measuring the rate of water flow through a turbine or water-wheel.

How It Works

The sensor is a Hall effect switch (see Section 1 above) of the type which operates as a normally-open switch and is sensitive to field strength. The magnet is mounted so that one end comes within 2–3mm of the centre of the IC as it sweeps past it. The IC has an open-collector output, so it needs a pull-up resistor (R1) to hold the output high (+12V) when the switch is off. Each time the magnet comes past the sensor the output falls to 0V. In this way a series of square-wave pulses is generated with frequency depending on the rate of rotation of the mechanism (Fig. 7.6).

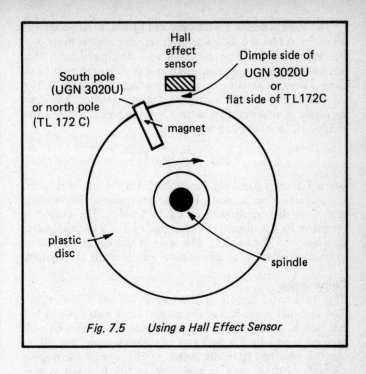

Fig. 7.5   Using a Hall Effect Sensor

The other IC is a frequency-to-voltage converter. Pulses or other regular wave-forms received at its input (pin 1) are converted into square waves by an operational amplifier connected as a Schmitt trigger. This is not necessary when the signal comes from a Hall effect switch, but the function is built in and can not be by-passed. The output of the amplifier goes to a charge pump, connected to pins 2 and 3. Each time a pulse is received, the charge pump adds to the charge accumulating on capacitor C3. The more pulses, the more charge is accumulated, the amount added each time being proportional to the capacitance of C2. The charge leaks away slowly through R6. The rate at which charge leaks away is inversely proportional to its resistance. Thus the charge on C3 builds up to a steady level, depending on the frequency of pulses, the capacitance of C2 and the resistance of R6.

The voltage across C3 is monitored by a second operational amplifier connected as a non-inverting amplifier with its output supplying the base current to an npn transistor. This allows for a higher-power output, and one that can be used to drive a device operating on a higher voltage (up to 30V). The internal circuit of IC2 has its own voltage reference, 7.56V, so its action is unaffected by battery level above about 10V. The output of the IC at pin 5 is given by:

$$V_{OUT} = 7.56 \times fRC$$

where f is the signal frequency in hertz (or the rate of rotation in revolutions per second), R is the resistance of R6 in ohms and C is the capacitance of C2 in farads. The output is measured by a voltmeter, which is made up of a microammeter in series with resistor R7. The scale of this can be marked to indicate frequency or revolutions per second, as required.

Construction

The mechanical aspects of this project are left to the reader. The essential point is that the magnet must pass close to but not touch the IC. It is important that the magnet be well secured, especially if a high rate of rotation is involved. If no signal is obtained from the output of IC1, reverse the magnet so that its other pole comes close to the IC. For greater sensitivity at low speeds, several magnets could be evenly spaced around the periphery of the disc.

The sensor is necessarily mounted on or close to the mechanism but the remainder of the circuit can be at a distance from it, connected by a twisted pair of wires. IC2 is available in 8-pin and 14-pin packages. The pin numbers given in Figure 7.6 are those for the 14-pin package. For the 8-pin version, the connections are:

14-pin version (Fig. 7.6)	8-pin version
1	1
2	2
3	3
4	3

14-pin version	8-pin version	
(Fig. 7.6)		
5	4	
8	5	
9	6	
10	7	
11	8	
12	8	(omit D1)

The values for C2 and R6 depend on the range of speeds that are to be measured. Any reasonable pair of values can be used, the only point to remember being that the maximum output voltage can be no more than about 6.4V. Suggested values which give a maximum of 6.2V are:

Frequency range (Hz)	C2 (nF)	R6
0 – 10	100	820kΩ
0 – 100	10	820kΩ
0 – 1000	10	82kΩ

As this is a precision circuit, with linearity about 0.3%, it is feasible to use high-precision components for C2 and R6. If 1% precision is required (it is not possible to read the meter with higher precision than this), use a 1% metal film resistor for R6. Use a 1% tolerance polystyrene capacitor for C2. These are obtainable in 10nF capacitance, but not so easily obtainable in 100n capacitance.

The value of R7 can be calculated from:

$$R = V_{MAX}/I - r$$

where V_{MAX} is the maximum value of the output of IC2 for a given range of frequency, I is the full-scale current reading of the meter in amps, and r is the resistance of the meter coil in ohms. For example, with a maximum output of 6.2V, using a 100μA meter, coil resistance 3750Ω, we calculate $R = 6.2/(100 \times 10^{-6}) - 3750 = 58250Ω$. For 1% precision use a precision resistor. A 59kΩ metal film resistor with 0.1% tolerance is suggested.

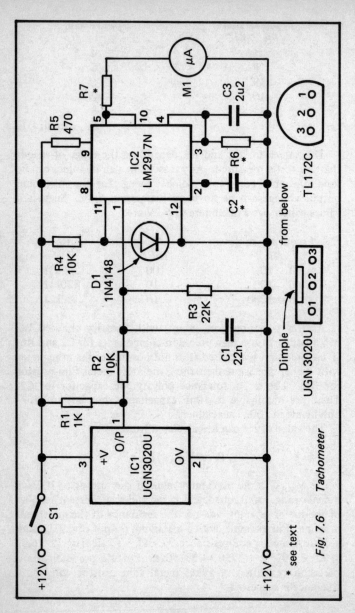

Fig. 7.6 Tachometer

* see text

Details of Special Parts

Integrated Circuits

IC1   UGN3020U or TL172C Hall effect switch

IC2   LM2917N tachometer or frequency-to-voltage converter.

Chapter 8

SOME MORE SENSORS

In this chapter we describe a range of sensors for many different measurands, illustrating to the full the ingenuity and inventiveness that had been applied to this branch of technology.

1 Humidity sensors

Humidity or relative humidity, which is the frequently used measure of humidity, is the amount of water vapour held in the air, relative to the maximum amount that would be held in saturated air at the same temperature. It is usually expressed as a percentage, ranging from 0% for absolutely dry air, to 100% for saturated air. The measurement of relative humidity is important not only for meterological purposes but also for controlling air conditioning systems. In libraries, computer rooms, and in certain types of warehouses, the maintenance of the correct humidity is of particular concern.

Since relative humidity depends both on the quantity of water vapour in a given volume of air, and also on the temperature of the air, it is not a simple quantity to measure. One approach is to use two thermometers, one with an exposed bulb and the other with the bulb covered with a wick saturated with water. These are the well-known *wet and dry bulb thermometers*. The difference between their temperature is a measure of the rate of evaporation of the water, which is in turn related to the relative humidity. The relationship is complicated; charts have been computed to convert the two temperature readings to relative humidity. Electronic instruments based on this principle are available, usually with two platinum resistance thermometers (page 43).

The alternative approach to measuring humidity relies on the use of hygroscopic materials. These are materials which absorb water to an extent depending on the humidity of the air around them. As humidity falls, the water is desorbed and evaporates from them. The change in the amount of water

129

held by these *hygroscopic materials* is accompanied by a change in some measurable physical property. Most non-electronic hygrometers use bundles of human hair. The change in length of the hair with variations in humidity are used to move a pointer round a dial. Electronic hygrometers use thin layers of hygroscopic substances such as salts of aluminium and measure the effect of absorbed water on their resistance or capacitance. Figure 8.1 illustrates a capacitative hygrometer. The porous electrode is a very thin layer of gold,

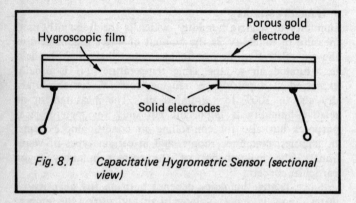

Fig. 8.1   Capacitative Hygrometric Sensor (sectional view)

which allows water to be absorbed by the aluminium oxide or to evaporate from it. The sensor acts as two variable capacitors in series, and their combined capacitance is a measure of humidity. Figure 8.2 shows a resistive hygrometer in which there are two electrodes printed on a plastic base, the element then being coated with a film of a hygroscopic salt.

A third type of hygrometric sensor has a quartz crystal coated with a layer of hygroscopic salt. The crystal is part of an oscillator circuit and its resonant frequency depends on the amount of water absorbed by the salt. By measuring this frequency we have a measure of humidity. Once again we see that three basic electrical properties, resistance, capacitance and e.m.f. production, can all be put to use in determining a single measurand.

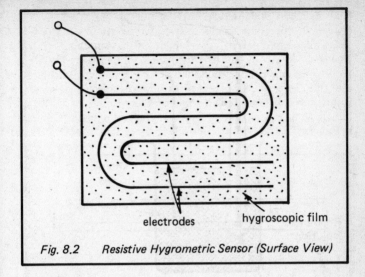

electrodes   hygroscopic film

Fig. 8.2   Resistive Hygrometric Sensor (Surface View)

2 pH sensors

The degree of acidity or alkalinity of a solution is measured on the pH scale, which is itself a measure of the hydrogen ion concentration in the solution. The scale ranges from pH0, which is strongly acid, through pH7, which is neutral, to pH14, which is strongly alkaline. We measure pH by immersing two electrodes in the test solution (Fig. 8.3), though more often the two electrodes are combined into a single probe. The electrodes are usually of platinum wire to resist corrosion. One electrode is surrounded by a standard solution of an electrolyte and is separated from the solution under test by an envelope of very thin glass. The glass is semi-permeable, allowing hydrogen ions to diffuse through it, in preference to ions of other types. A p.d. develops between the electrodes and this is measured by a millivoltmeter with high-impedance input. The display scale reads pH directly, though the instrument needs calibration in standard solutions of known pH before use. Probes are also available with membranes selectively permeable to other ions such as K^+ (potassium), Cl^- (chlorine), and Cu^{++} (copper) so that similar methods can be used to measure concentrations of these ions.

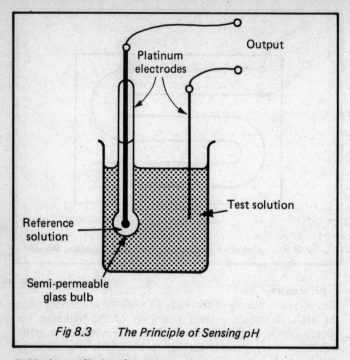

Fig 8.3   *The Principle of Sensing pH*

Labels in figure: Output; Platinum electrodes; Test solution; Reference solution; Semi-permeable glass bulb

3 Nuclear radiation detectors

There are various types of nuclear radiation:

α particles — helium nuclei, positively charged
β particles — electrons, negatively charged
γ radiation — electromagnetic radiation of very short
    wavelength
protons, positively charged particles
neutrons, uncharged particles.

All these types of radiation, except for neutrons, cause the formation of ions as they pass through matter. This action provides the basis of techniques for measuring nuclear radiation. Figure 8.4 illustrates a typical sensor, an ionisation chamber. It contains an inert gas such as argon or krypton under low pressure. The two electrodes have a high p.d.

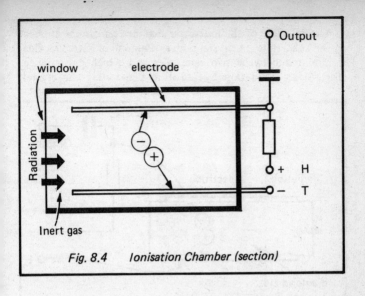

Fig. 8.4   Ionisation Chamber (section)

between them, of several hundred volts. One end of the chamber is made of thin metal to allow radiation to penetrate; this is known as the *window*. If the chamber is to detect α-radiation, which is absorbed by even a thin layer of metal, the window is made of mica. When ionising radiation passes into the chamber it causes the production of pairs of ions. The positive ion of each pair is attracted toward the negative electrode and the negative ion is attracted toward the positive electrode.

If the chamber is operated in current mode, we measure the current passing through the chamber as a result of the flow of ions. In pulse-mode (illustrated in Figure 8.4) a single ionisation-results in a pulse which is detected by circuitry connected to the capacitor. If the p.d. is relatively low, the size of the current or pulses is related to the type of ionising radiation, so it is possible to discriminate between the types, and to measure the energies of the particles. If a higher p.d. is used, the ions formed by radiation collide violently with atoms of gas, creating more ion pairs. There is an avalanche effect, increasing the sensitivity of the chamber; the pulse size is proportional to the energy of the particles.

The principle of the ionisation chamber can also be applied to the solid state. A crystal such as diamond or silver chloride is mounted between two electrodes and a high p.d. applied (Fig. 8.5). Ionisation by radiation penetrating the crystal

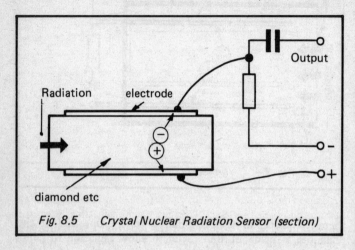

Fig. 8.5   Crystal Nuclear Radiation Sensor (section)

causes the production of a current or pulses as in the ionisation chamber. Another type of solid-state sensor employs a slice of semiconductor material. This may be intrinsic (pure) silicon or germanium, or extrinsic (doped) semiconductor, as in Figure 8.6. Ionisation results in the creation of electron-hole pairs and the consequent flow of current or pulses.

The Geiger-Muller tube (Fig. 8.7) is a type of gas ionisation chamber, which is operated at the maximum p.d. that does not actually result in continuous electrical discharge through the gas. The gas has a quenching vapour such as alcohol or bromine mixed with it to damp out any continuous discharge that might occur. The avalanche effect gives this tube high sensitivity but, since the p.d. is above the Geiger plateau, its response is independent of the nature of the radiation or the energy of the particles.

A scintillation detector works on an entirely different principle. At one end of the counter is a screen coated with a scintillator substance such as zinc sulphide (Fig. 8.8). When

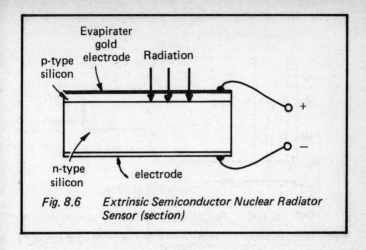

Fig. 8.6   Extrinsic Semiconductor Nuclear Radiator
Sensor (section)

radiation falls on the screen, small flashes or scintillations are produced. The number of flashes in a given time interval is proportional to the intensity of the radiation. With low level radiation, the scintillations can be observed by eye and counted individually. A more reliable method is to use a photomultiplier (page 27) to detect the scintillations automatically.

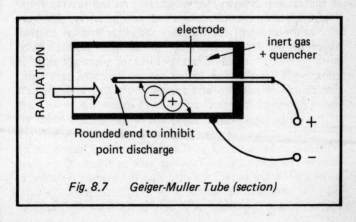

Fig. 8.7   Geiger-Muller Tube (section)

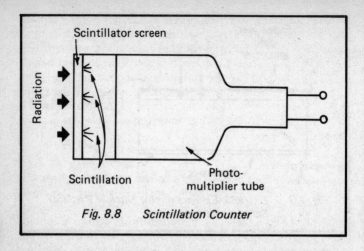

Fig. 8.8   Scintillation Counter

Neutrons are uncharged so they have no ionising effect and are not as easily detectable as other forms of nuclear radiation. One method of detecting them is to direct the neutron beam at a target containing certain isotopes of lithium or boron. The nuclei of the isotope atoms absorb neutrons readily, and then disintegrates, emitting ionising particles, which can be detected in the usual way.

Measurement of nuclear radiation is of obvious importance in the nuclear industry, for monitoring nuclear reactions, for experimental measurements and for ensuring safety. Monitoring the environment for excessive radiation levels is another important use for such sensors. In biological research, very small amounts of radioactive isotopes of elements such as phosphorus, carbon and iodine are incorporated into compounds fed to experimental animals (including humans) and plants. Radiation sensors are used to follow the movements of these substances inside the plant or animal and hence to investigate aspects of metabolism. In medicine, radioactive substances are used in similar ways in the diagnosis of disease. Gamma-radiating isotopes such as cobalt-60 are used instead of X-ray tubes. In medicine the gamma radiation is used for treatment of cancer, while in industry it may be used for examining forged metal structures for flaws for example.

There are many other industrial applications; for example, the thickness of polythene film coming from a mill is measured continuously by detecting the amount of radiation penetrating the film from a radioactive source placed behind it. Another typical application is described on page 149. The dating of rocks and archaeological remains by measuring the amounts of certain radioactive elements present, is another sphere of scientific investigation that depends on radiation sensors.

4 Gas sensors

One popular example of gas sensor contains two elements, the sensor and the compensator, enclosed beneath a dome of stainless steel mesh. The mesh is to prevent explosions possibly being caused by the combustion within the dome spreading to an inflammable atmosphere outside. The elements comprise two heater coils made of fine platinum wire and coated with special mixtures of metal oxides and catalysts. The mixture around the sensor element is compounded so that when current passing through the element raises its temperature to $350°C$, certain combustible gases that might be in the air are adsorbed on to the surface of the element and oxidised. The other element also has current passing through it to keep its temperature at $350°C$, and acts to compensate for changes in ambient temperature and humidity. The coating on this element does not have the catalysts that bring about oxidation of combustible gases. In the presence of such gases, oxidation on the sensor element results in heat production, raising the temperature of the sensor above $350°C$. This increases the resistivity of the platinum wire. The sensor and compensator are connected in a half-bridge (Fig. 1.8(b)) which is balanced in the absence of combustible gases. The presence of the gases is detected by the bridge going out of balance. Gases that are detectable by sensors such as this include isobutane, methane (present in natural gas and town gas), hydrogen and ethanol (alcohol). A project based on this sensor appears at the end of this chapter.

137

PROJECT 10 – Gas Alarm (Level 2)

This uses one of the gas sensors described in Section 4 above to detect when appreciable amounts of combustible gas are present in the atmosphere. The circuit has obvious applications in the home, garage, caravan or boat. When gas is detected, a bleeper sounds intermittently and two LEDs flash on and off, alternating with each other to produce an attention-catching display. The alarm continues until the gas has been removed and the reset button has been pressed.

How It Works

In Figure 8.9 the gas sensing devices are represented by the two resistors R2 and R3, the sensor and compensator. They are connected in a half-bridge (page 14), the other two arms of the bridge being made up of R4, R5 and VR2. The current to power the bridge and to heat the filaments is provided from a variable voltage regulator, IC1, the voltage supplied being adjusted by setting VR1. The constant voltage ensures that the filaments are maintained steadily at the correct operating temperature. In the absence of gases the voltage between R2 and R3 is approximately half the voltage from the regulator. This is fed to the (+) input of the operational amplifier IC2, which is being used as a comparator.

The bridge is almost balanced by turning VR2 until the voltage at its wiper, and also at the (−) input of the amplifier is about 20mV below that at the (+) input. Under these conditions the output of the amplifier swings high (to +6V). When gas is present R2 becomes hotter and its resistance increases, lowering the voltage at the (+) input. After the voltage has fallen by a little more than 20mV the (−) input is then at a higher level than the (+) input and the output of the amplifier falls to 0V.

The output of the amplifier is compatible with the logic circuits that follow. The first logic stage is a flip-flop, consisting of two cross-connected NAND gates. Normally its inputs are both held high but, when gas is detected and the amplifier output goes low, the flip-flop becomes set. Its output goes high and this enables an astable multivibrator, also consisting of two NAND gates labelled A and B in Figure 8.9. The frequency of the astable is about 1Hz. When the astable is not running the output of gate A is high and that of gate B is low. Current flows from gate A to TR3 turning it on and making the LED D1 glow continuously. Since the output of gate B is low, the other LED D2 is off and the AWD is silent. When gas is detected and the astable is enabled, the output of gates A and B go high alternately, flashing D1 and D2, and making the AWD sound intermittently.

The LEDs flash and the AWD sounds until the S2 is pressed to reset the flip-flop, or the power is switched off.

The transistors are drawn in Figure 8.9 as if they are single transistors but the MPSA13 actually consists of two npn transistors connected as a Darlington pair. It has very high gain and this means that the base resistor can be of relatively high value, drawing only a small current from the logic gates.

Construction

The sensors require 150mA or more, so this circuit is best powered from a 6V DC mains adaptor. In a caravan or boat it may be powered from the storage battery, but care must be taken not to exhaust this if it is not recharged daily. Sensors vary in the amount of current they require; if it is important to be economical of current, select a type with relatively low current requirements. A current of 140mA is probably the minimum. If you are using a mains adaptor, check that it can supply the required current without loss of voltage. Many of the cheaper models supply only 300mA and, if heavy-current sensors are used, this may not be quite enough. The circuit also runs on a 12V DC supply; in this case use 220Ω resistors for R12 and R13.

The sensor and comparator are supplied as separate units or both are housed beneath a single mesh dome. The separate units are generally sold as a matched pair, with identical appearance except for distinguishing markings. The sensor and comparator are to be mounted on the outside of the case, or just inside it, close to perforations which supply ample ventilation.

First wire up the voltage regulator circuit, consisting of IC1, C1, VR1 and R1. The regulator requires a small heat-sink. Switch on the power and adjust VR1 to supply the

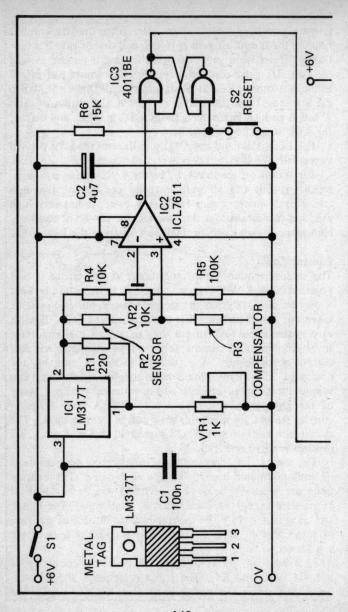

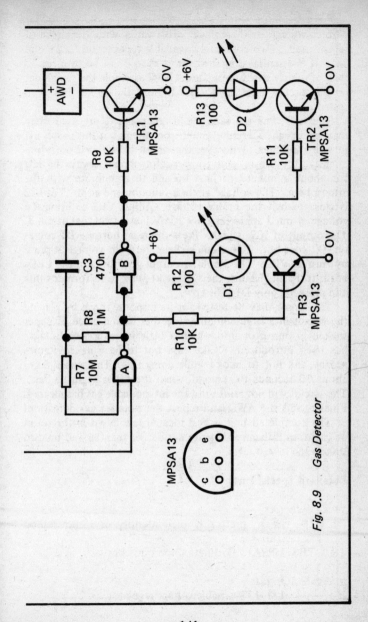

Fig. 8.9   Gas Detector

141

correct voltage to the bridge. This varies with the make of sensor used. Two commonly available types require 2.2V and 3V. It is essential that the sensors should not be over-run as they are fairly easily burnt out. Now assemble the remainder of the circuit, omitting the AWD until the circuit has been tested.

The first time the sensor and compensator are used there may be a slight scorching smell from them, but this passes off in a few minutes. Whenever the circuit is switched on subsequently, the sensor and compensator should always be left for about a minute to heat up and to equilibrate with the atmosphere. The voltage at their junction and at pin 3 of IC2 is close to half the bridge voltage. Adjust VR2 to bring the voltage at pin 2 approximately 20mV lower than that at pin 3. The output of IC2 is high. Press the reset button. D1 comes on, D2 goes out. For a quick check, raise the voltage at pin 2 by turning VR2. The amplifier output goes low and the LEDs begin to flash. Return the voltage at pin 2 to its former value and press S1; only D1 is lit now.

The sensor may be tested for its response to gas by placing the circuit in a large container together with a piece of paper soaked in petrol or into which a little house gas or butagas has been introduced. Take care not to have naked flames nearby and not to smoke while doing this. The sensor takes about 10 seconds to respond, when the LEDs begin to flash. The circuit will not reset until the inflammable gas has cleared. Finally, add the AWD and repeat the tests for gas detection.

The completed unit is best located low down in the room or cabin, as inflammable gases are denser than air and tend to sink to the lowest level.

Details of Special Parts

Semiconductors
D1, D2   LEDs, preferably high-intensity or 10mm jumbo size
TR1–TR3 MPSA13 Darlington npn transistor

Integrated Circuits
IC1   LM317T variable voltage regulator

| IC2 | ICL7611 CMOS operational amplifier |
| IC3 | 4011BE CMOS quadruple 2-input NAND gate |

Miscellaneous

| AWD | Solid-state buzzer or sounder with a continuous note. |

Chapter 9

USING SENSORS

Most of the sensors described in previous chapters are used to directly detect or measure a particular measurand. For example we have shown how to use a photodiode to measure light intensity, and how to use a thermistor to measure temperature. Sensors may be used indirectly also. From their response to their primary measurand we are able to detect or measure some *other* physical quantity. Several examples occurred in Chapter 4. There we saw how a strain gauge, which primarily measures the distortion of a mechanical structure under force, can also be used to measure weight. There is no sensor that responds to weight as such but, by using a strain gauge to measure the distortion of a load cell (page 65) we are able to measure the weight of the object it is supporting. This theme is taken up as the subject of this chapter. There is no sharp dividing line between the direct use and indirect use of sensors, but in this chapter we have a range of examples to illustrate the indirect approach. There are so many ways in which sensors are used indirectly that it is not possible to cover them all. Here we pick our examples from a few fields of measurement, and this serves to show what a variety of techniques have been invented in the application of sensors.

1 Tachometers

Tachometers are instruments used to measure rates of rotation. Project 9 (page 122) is a tachometer in which the sensor involved is a Hall effect device. It would have been possible, though rather less convenient, to use an electromagnetic coil instead, detecting changes in its self-inductance (page 80). In either case we require a circuit to count the number of pulses coming from the sensor in a given period of time, and to display the result as revolutions per minute or per second.

Light sensors may also be used in tachometers, using a rotary encoder (page 89). An alternative is a reflectance method in which pulses of light reflected from a rotating toothed wheel or sectored disc are detected by a sensor and converted into electrical pulses.

A different approach is based on the stroboscope. A toothed wheel, or a disc painted with radial stripes, rotates in front of a stroboscopic lamp. The lamp flashes brightly at a precisely known rate. Often a xenon tube is used. The rate of flashing is adjusted until the angle of rotation between flashes is exactly equal to the angle between adjacent teeth or stripes. The wheel or disc then appears to be stationary. This technique has high precision; if the rate of flashing is not exactly correct, the wheel appears to turn either forward or backward. It lends itself to automatic control, with a photo-sensitive device to detect when the radial pattern is stationary.

2 Fluid flow meters

One of the simplest methods of measuring the rate of flow of liquids or gases is to place a propellor in the flowing stream and measure its rate of rotation. The term 'propellor' includes not only the two-bladed structure looking like the propellor of a boat or aeroplane, but also the 3- or 4-cupped rotor of the anemometer (page 122) and various forms of multi-bladed turbine. The rate of rotation is measured by a tacho-meter, described above, and the prime sensing method may be magnetic (Hall effect), self-inductive, or optical.

Figure 9.1 illustrates a variety of other flow-measuring techniques. In Figure 9.1(a) there is a plate across the tube in which the fluid is flowing. An orifice restricts the flow so that pressure becomes greater on one side of the plate than on the other. The pressure difference is measured by a pressure sensor, such as that shown in Figure 4.7. The inequality of pressure on opposite sides of the diaphragm causes it to bulge one way to the other and thus affects the capacitance of the sensor. Another device depending on pressure differ-ence to measure flow is the pitot tube (Fig. 9.1(b)). This is frequently used to measure air speed of aeroplanes. The pitot tube consists of two concentric tubes, the inner one of which is open and receives the full pressure due to the air current. The outer one is perforated on its sides and thus the air in this tube is at ambient pressure. A differential pressure sensor is used to measure the pressure difference, which is then

146

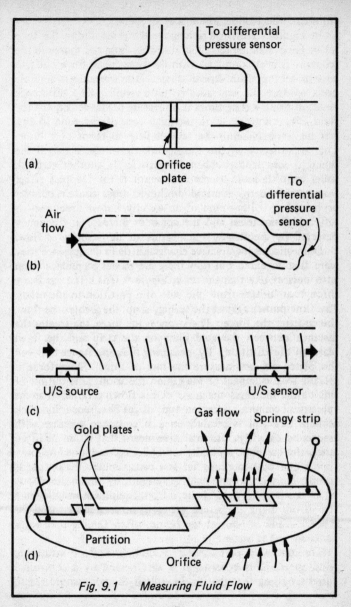

(a) Orifice plate

To differential pressure sensor

(b) Air flow

To differential pressure sensor

(c) U/S source   U/S sensor

(d) Gold plates   Gas flow   Springy strip

Partition

Orifice

Fig. 9.1   Measuring Fluid Flow

converted to a reading in terms of air speed.

In Figure 9.1(c) flow is measured by measuring the time taken for a burst of ultra-sound to pass from the source to the sensor. This is compared with the time taken for a burst to pass in the opposite direction, since the transducers are able both to transmit and receive ultra-sound. The difference between these transit times is a measure of the velocity of the fluid. We know the cross-sectional area of the tube so this can be converted into the rate of flow in terms of volume. The performance of this transit-time flowmeter is best if the liquid is free from bubbles or particles. Another method, using an ultra-sonic source and sensor is the Doppler effect flowmeter. In this method the liquid *must* contain bubbles or particles. Ultra-sound of an exactly known frequency is reflected from these and the apparent increase in frequency detected by the sensor is a measure of the velocity of flow.

Domestic gas meters have changed little in design since they were first invented but now there are moves to replace them with devices like that shown in Figure 9.1(d). The gas flows through an orifice from one side of a partition to the other. The flow pushes against the springy strip, the greater the flow, the stronger the force. The stronger the force, the greater the distance between the gold plate on the strip and the fixed plate on the partition. By measuring the capacitance between the plates we can measure the rate of flow. Since force is related to the impact of the gas on the spring, the output of this device measures the mass of gas flowing rather than its velocity or volume. This new type of gas flow sensor has been miniaturised and fabricated on a silicon chip together with associated circuitry. Its small size means that it can be fitted *inside* the gas pipe, replacing the bulky old-fashioned bellows-type meter by something far less conspicuous. Its output is compatible with remote-reading systems, by which the meters of houses in a street can be read from equipment installed in a van driven along the street. There is no longer any need for a meter-reader to call at the house, often finding that occupants are not at home.

The hot wire anemometer is another way of measuring wind speed. This consists of a wire heated by a controlled current passing through it. In still air the wire would reach, and be maintained at, a constant known temperature. The wire is exposed to the wind, which removes heat from it. This lowers its temperature, which is measured by treating it as a resistance thermometer (page 43). The temperature reading is then converted into wind speed. A similar principle is used to measure flow of fluids in a tube. A heater coil is mounted centrally in the tube with a thermocouple a short distance on either side of it. The 'upstream' thermocouple measures the fluid temperature before it reaches the heater, and the 'downstream' thermocouple measures its temperature after it has passed the heater. By comparing the two temperature measurements it is possible to calculate the rate of flow. This technique is used both for gases and liquids.

Wind-chill depends on wind velocity and also on the interaction of factors such as air temperature, the range of wind speeds over a given period of time and to what extent the flow is steadily directed or gusty. One way of assessing the effect of this rather unpredictable combination of factors is shown in Figure 9.2. Heater coils supply heat to an exposed metal surface at a known rate. The temperature of the surface is measured by a thermistor. The measurement embodies the essential nature of wind-chill, the removal of heat from a warm surface.

3 Liquid level sensors

Under this heading we include the sensing of levels of powdered or granular solids. The methods described in this section well underline the fact that many different kinds of sensor may be utilised for the same purpose. Figure 9.3 shows a few examples. A straightforward resistive technique is shown in Figure 9.3(a), suitable for conductive liquids. The circuit is completed when the level rises to immerse the tips of the contacts. It is usual to apply an alternating p.d. to the contacts so that electrolytic effects do not occur, which might lead, for example, to plating of one of the contacts. A project based on this principle appears at the end of the chapter.

In Figure 9.3(b) the beam of IR between source and sensor is broken when the liquid level rises. Similar methods are used with beams of ultra-sound, gamma-rays (page 132) or microwaves, and are applicable to powdered or granular solids too.

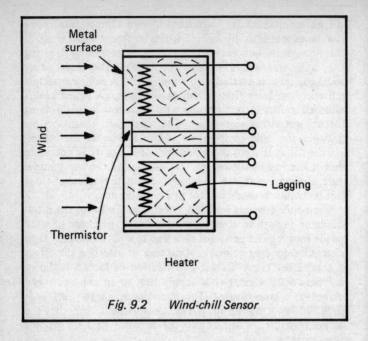

Metal surface

Wind

Thermistor

Lagging

Heater

Fig. 9.2   Wind-chill Sensor

All of these methods detect a point level, such as when a tank or hopper is full or empty. The depth of liquid may be measured at any level by the methods shown in Figure 9.3(c) and 9.3(d). Here the time is measured for a pulse of ultra-sound to return to the sensor after being reflected from the liquid surface. In the second case the difference of time between reflection from the surface and from the bottom of the tank is measured.

A capacitance level sensor is shown in Figure 9.3(e). The conductive capacitor plates are on the outside of the glass. As the liquid rises and falls the capacitance between the plates increases and decreases, and can be measured in one of the usual ways.

Various mechanical methods are also used. The pressure produced by the head of liquid in the tank can be sensed by a pressure sensor mounted at the bottom of the tank. The density of the liquid is known so that the depth of liquid can

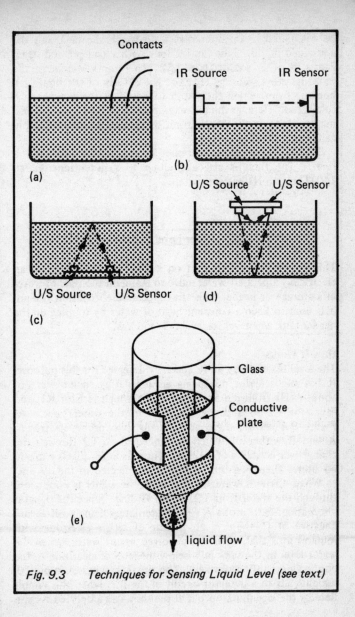

Fig. 9.3   Techniques for Sensing Liquid Level (see text)

Contacts

(a)

IR Source   IR Sensor

(b)

U/S Source   U/S Sensor

(c)

U/S Source   U/S Sensor

(d)

Glass

Conductive plate

liquid flow

(e)

be calculated. An alternative is to weigh the tank and the contained liquid. This can be done with a load cell and strain gauge or other sensor (page 65). The empty weight of the tank, its cross-sectional area and the density of the liquid are known, from which the depth of liquid in the tank can be calculated. Here, as in most examples above, the 'calculations' may be done partly by electronic means and partly by suitably calibrating the display dial.

Finally, the level can be sensed by gauging the position of a float. The float is attached either to a potentiometer, an LVDT or to a Hall-effect switch.

PROJECT 11 – Water Level Controller (Level 2)

This circuit is used to turn on a small electric pump or an electrically operated water valve to maintain the level of water in a storage or header tank. In a greenhouse irrigation system, it is used to keep a constant head of water by topping up the header tank whenever its level falls too low.

How It Works

The level is sensed by an IC specially designed for this purpose. It has an oscillator producing an alternating square wave of about 6kHz from pin 5. This is fed through resistor R1, and capacitor C2 to a probe electrode in the water tank. As Figure 9.4 shows, there are actually two probe electrodes, A and B, either of which is connected to C2 through the changeover contacts of a relay. The reason for this is explained later. There is a third probe, C, connected to the 0V line.

When there is water in the tank, the signal is conducted through the water from C2 to the 0V line. Since the signal is alternating, with probe A (or B) alternately being positive and negative of C, there is no plating of either electrode with mineral ions that might be dissolved in the water. When the water level in the tank falls below the level of electrode A, the connection to 0V is broken. The signal then passes to pin 10, which leads to a detector circuit in the IC. When this circuit detects the signal, its output at pin shows an amplified version

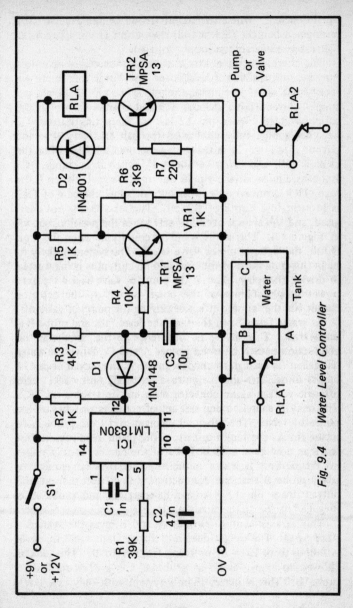

Fig. 9.4   Water Level Controller

153

of the signal. When the signal is not being detected (for example, when the tank is full) the output at pin 12 remains high (approximately the supply voltage).

The alternating output from pin 12 is intended to operate a buzzer to warn that the level is too low, but in this circuit we rectify this signal to control a relay. When pin 12 is high, the supply current flows through R3 and charges C3 up to the supply voltage. When pin 12 has an alternating output, C3 becomes almost fully discharged through D1 every time the output goes low. Thus the voltage across C3 is high when the tank is full, and drops to about 1V when it is empty. C3 smooths almost all the ripple due to the signal. When C3 is high, TR1 is turned on and its output is low; the base of TR2 is brought low, turning TR2 off. The relay coil is not energised, and the change-over contacts are in the positions shown in Figure 9.4. This is the stand-by condition: when the tank is full, the water-pump or valve is off. The system is likely to be in this state most of the time and no current is being wasted in driving the relay. Also, if the pump or valve have a separate power supply, failure of the power supply to the detector circuit has the fail-safe effect of turning the pump or valve off.

As water flows from the tank the level falls and probe B is uncovered. This makes no difference to the circuit, as the conduction path is between probes A and C. When the water has fallen far enough to uncover probe A, the output at pin 12 begins to oscillate and the voltage across C2 falls. TR1 turns off, the voltage at its collector rises and this turns on TR2. The relay is energised and one set of contacts switches on the pump or valve. The other set changes over from probe A to probe B. As the tank begins to refill, probe A is covered but this has now been switched out of the circuit, so this makes no difference. It is not until the water rises far enough to cover probe B that the conduction path is restored and the output from pin 12 becomes de-energised and probe A is switched back into the circuit again.

This arrangement of probes A and B gives the system a *dead band*. The circuit does not change state while the level is falling from B to A, or rising from A to B. The tank is allowed to empty as far as probe A, and is then refilled to probe B. This is better than a system with only one level-sensing probe as the system would switch on as soon as that probe was uncovered only to switch off again a moment later as the first few drops of water started to refill the tank. The system would oscillate, with consequent wear on relay contacts and other undesirable effects.

Construction

The IC requires a minimum of 9V, so a 9V or 12V supply is the most suitable. The circuit requires about 13mA when quiescent and about 35mA (depending upon the resistance of the relay coil) when the relay is energised. Although the system can be powered from heavy-duty dry cells or rechargeable lead-acid batteries, a 12V DC mains adaptor is preferred.

The probes are easily made from insulated tinned copper wire with a few millimetres of insulation stripped from the ends. Although Figure 9.4 shows probes A and B passing through the side of the tank, it is easier to fix the three probes to a strip of plastic (Fig. 9.5) immersed in the tank.

Assemble the first section of the circuit, as far as R3 and C2. At this stage use temporary probes; two bare-ended wires dipping into a bowl of water. Check that the voltage at the junction of R3 and C2 is high when both probes are in the water and goes low when one of them is removed. Complete the circuit, apart from connecting the probes to the relay. Adjust VR1 so that TR2 turns on and the relay is activated when one or other of the temporary probes is removed from the water, but is off when both are immersed. If VR1 is properly adjusted, the voltage at its wiper is about 0.1V with the probes immersed and about 1.5V with one removed.

Finally connect the permanent probes to the relay, and connect the pump or valve to the other set of contacts.

Details of Special Parts

Semiconductors
D1   1N4148 silicon signal diode
D2   1N4001 silicon rectifier diode
TR1, TR2 MPSA13 npn Darlington pair

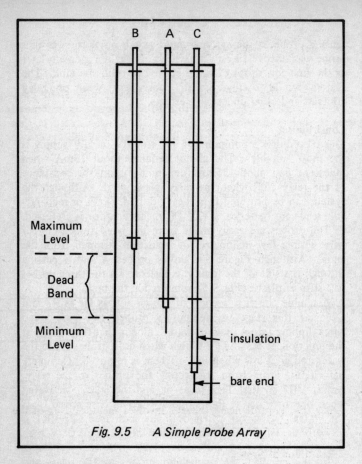

Fig. 9.5   A Simple Probe Array

Integrated Circuits
IC1   LM1830N water level sensor IC

Miscellaneous
RLA   12V relay with two change-over sets of contacts.

Chapter 10

SENSORS AND SYSTEMS

Having studied a very wide range of sensors in previous chapters we are now ready to return to and expand upon some of the themes developed in Chapter 1. As was stated in that chapter, the purposes for which sensors are used fall under two principal headings:

1 Measurement
To obtain quantitative information about a given measurand. Sometimes measurement is required over a range of values, as with a thermometer. Sometimes we need only a point measurement, as with a fire alarm triggered by a snap-action switching thermal sensor.

2 Control
To regulate the level of a physical quantity. Often the quantity is regulated to a constant level, for example a thermostat, but it may also be continuously regulated to a changing level, as with a power-assisted steering mechanism, or a synchro system (page 77).

There are instances in which it is not easy to decide whether a sensor and the circuit associated with it are being used for measurement or for control. This follows from the fact that control nearly always involves measurement of the quantity being controlled.

Measurement Systems
Figure 10.1 illustrates the essential parts of a basic electronic measurement system. These are the sensor to respond to the measurand, the display unit which indicates the present level (and possibly previous levels) of the measurand, and the processing circuits which converts the output from the sensor into a form suitable to drive the display.

Sensors have been dealt with in detail in the previous chapters. Their most desirable features are that they should have a suitably wide response range and a linear response

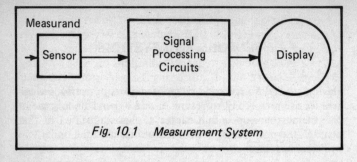

Fig. 10.1   Measurement System

(page 4) over the whole of that range.

Processing (or signal conditioning) circuits range in complexity from a single resistor (Fig. 1.6) to an array of operational amplifiers and other sub-circuits intended to compensate for the idiosyncrasies of the sensor and the vagaries of the environment, and to display the results in a form suiting the requirements and preferences of the human operator. The first stage of processing is usually the conversion of the output of the sensor into a varying voltage. Methods for doing this were described in Chapter 1. This stage may include impedance matching, so that the signal from the sensor is not just 'absorbed' into subsequent circuits without producing a measurable effect.

Many measurement systems include one or more stages of amplification. This is necessary if the e.m.f. from the sensor is too small to drive the display. It is also used to set the scale, fitting the full output of the processing circuit to the maximum reading of the display meter.

Another important aspect of processing is to remove unwanted signals that somehow or other become introduced into the system. An example is mains hum picked up by electromagnetic microphones. This is removed by passing the signal through a filter, so that frequencies in the region of 50Hz are eliminated from it. On occasions we may wish to pick out one particular frequency from a number of others that are present. In measuring 'brain waves', the alternating electrical potentials found in the brain, we use a band-pass filter to pick out waves of the particular frequency we wish to study. In this way the *theta* waves at 5–6Hz for example, are measured against a background of other waves of lower and higher frequencies. Similarly, in a seismometer, low-frequency waves caused by Earth movements can be passed to the next stage of processing while higher-frequency vibrations caused by passing traffic are filtered out. If processing is a matter of picking out one particular frequency, as opposed to suppressing one or more unwanted frequencies, it is also possible to use a frequency-dependent circuit such as a phase-locked loop. The whistle sensor of Project 8 is based on this principle.

Processing can also be used to compensate for certain features or deficiencies of the sensor. Most commonly required is compensation for variations in temperature of the sensor or its leads. This is often provided for at the earliest stage of processing by using a bridge (page 15). Another method is to avoid temperature variations by enclosing the sensor in an 'oven'. This is a small thermally insulated compartment held at a constant temperature, usually a little higher than the maximum ambient temperature.

A sensor may not produce a zero output when the measurand is at its zero level. An example is the LM335Z precision temperature sensor with an output proportional to temperature on the kelvin scale. At $0°C$ its output is 2.73V, and rises by 0.01V for every degree. To display the Celsius temperature, we need to subtract 2.73V from its output. Similarly, the MPX100AP pressure sensor has an output of 20mV at zero pressure. One way of subtracting a constant amount from the output is to use an operational amplifier as a summer, as in Figure 10.2. Summation occurs at the (−) input. Current flows through R1 to the input from the sensor, and a current flows away from the input through R2 to a point held at an offset reference voltage, R2. The output of the amplifier is $-(V_{SENSOR} - V_{OFFSET})$. The fact that the signal is inverted at this stage is immaterial, as it can be restored in a subsequent stage of processing.

Subtracting a zero offset voltage is an example of the numerous techniques for processing the signal mathematically before presenting it to the display. Another example is amplifying to produce a suitable range of output, as already mentioned. Mathematical processing may become more complex if the measurement of one measurand is to be used to

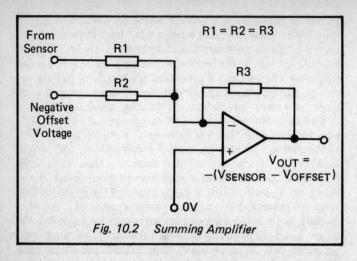

Fig. 10.2   Summing Amplifier

calculate the value of a related measurand. For example, measurements of the *position* of a moving object made by a position sensor can be converted to indicate the *velocity* of the object. Usually we do not want to wait until the motion is completed and then calculate the velocity. We need a continuous read-out of the velocity while the object is in motion. This may be done by continually computing the *rate of change* of position. Mathematically, this process is known as *differentiation* and it is done electronically by an operational amplifier connected as a differentiator (Fig. 10.3). The input signal is V_{IN}, which represents the position of the object and which is varying with time, the output signal is V_{OUT}. Since point A is a virtual earth, the feedback current $I_f = -V_{OUT}/R$. The input current I_{IN} determines the rate at which the capacitor becomes charged, so $I_{IN} = C.dV_{IN}/dt$. The two currents are equal and thus:

$$\frac{-V_{OUT}}{R} = C \cdot \frac{DV_{IN}}{dt}$$

and

$$V_{OUT} = -RC \frac{dV_{IN}}{dt}$$

160

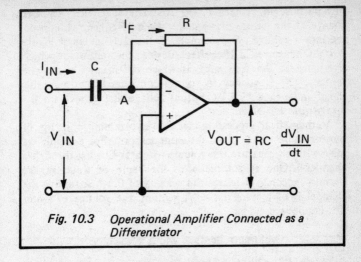

Fig. 10.3 *Operational Amplifier Connected as a Differentiator*

In this way the circuit produces an output voltage that is proportional to the *rate of change* of the input voltage. In other words, it is proportional to the rate of change of position of the object — its *velocity*. Since the acceleration of an object is the rate of change of its velocity, the output of the differentiator may be fed to a second differentiator to obtain an output proportional to acceleration.

The reverse process of differentiation is integration, which is performed by a circuit similar to that of Figure 10.3 in which R and C are interchanged. For this circuit the output voltage is:

$$- \frac{1}{RC} \int V_{IN} . dt$$

A circuit such as this can be used to sum the changing value of a measurand over a period of time, for example to obtain a mean value, eliminating short-term variations.

Processing a signal may sometimes require that its nature is changed. For example, an alternating signal may need to be rectified so that the DC voltage produced can be used to drive a voltmeter as the display unit. A precision rectifier is used for this purpose in Project 7, the sound level meter. Another change of the nature of a signal is when a frequency is converted into a voltage. For example, in the tachometer of Figure 7.6 the sensor is a Hall-effect device, the output of which alternates at the frequency at which the magnet passes the sensor. The frequency to voltage converter IC2 accepts this signal and produces a DC output voltage that varies with the *rate of rotation of the disc.*

Mathematical processing can also involve multiplication of two or more signals from different sensors. For example we may wish to measure the volume of water flowing through a channel. One sensor measures the depth of water in the channel; another measures the velocity of flow. Assuming the channel is of rectangular cross section, the volume of water flowing per second is:

$$\text{volume} = \text{depth} \times \text{width} \times \text{velocity}$$

Calculations of this type can be performed instanteously using an *analogue function module.* This is an integrated circuit that accepts two or more analogue input voltages and produces an output voltage that is equal to the product or some other function of the inputs. A typical device of this kind can accept up to 3 varying inputs, and multiply, divide, square or square-root them in various combinations. It can also multiply the result by a constant factor which could, for example, be the channel width in the equation above.

So far we have been concerned with processing analogue signals such as voltages, which vary smoothly over a given range. Many measurement systems operate with digital signals, the values being coded as binary numbers. Even in a digital system, the signal usually begins as a voltage from a sensor or a bridge circuit. Possibly after a few preliminary stages to amplify the voltage or to remove interference from it, the signal is converted into binary form by an *analogue to digital converter.* Here one important consideration is the number of binary digits (bits) in the output of the converter. An 8-bit converter produces only 256 distinct values, so the resolution of such a system may be too low for many purposes. Twelve or more bits are more commonly used.

After converting the signal into digital form, further processing is done by logic circuits. The complexity of the logic may range from a few relatively simple integrated circuits to a microprocessor-based system and even to a main-frame computer. These can be programmed to perform all the processing functions of the operational amplifier circuits already described above, and can do much more besides. It is an easy matter to convert values from one unit to another. Celsius temperatures can readily be converted to the Fahrenheit scale, and pressures measured in pascals can be converted to millibars. Mathematical processes such as multiplication, division, differentiation and integration can easily be performed. Thus we can have a car computer that not only displays the velocity but can work out the rate of fuel consumption, the estimated time of completion of the journey and the cost in pence per kilometre. With aeroplanes and spacecraft the possibilities are even more astounding. Mathematically averaging out a series of measurements taken over a period of time to smooth out short-term variations is the equivalent of filtering analogue signals. Although it is possible to build analogue circuits to store peak and trough values of a voltage (maxima and minima), such circuits are subject to errors. A computer can record and store a succession of such values with no problems at all.

Figure 10.4 shows an interesting technique for multiplying a digital signal (a) and an analogue voltage signal (b). The product (ab) is an analogue voltage ready for display by a voltmeter, or for further processing. The digital signal is fed to the inputs of an digital-to-analogue converter. Such converters operate by summing the currents passing through a 'ladder' of resistors. According to whether each bit in the digital value is '0' or '1' the corresponding weighted current is fed to the summer. The currents are generated by a standard voltage reference. One popular 8-bit D-to-A IC has a built-in 2.55V reference and this voltage would appear at the output if the digital input is 1111 1111 (= 255 decimal). For the 110101 (= 53) the output is 0.53V. In short, the output voltage is the binary input multiplied by 0.01. With many converters it is possible to use an external reference instead of the built-in reference. If the external reference is set to

163

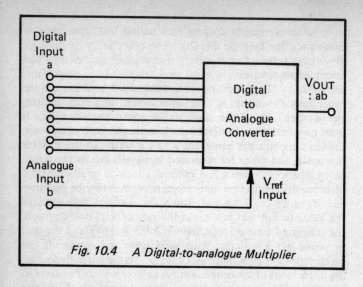

Fig. 10.4 *A Digital-to-analogue Multiplier*

5.10V for example, the output is the binary input multiplied by 0.02. This gives the basis for multiplication. By making the reference voltage proportional to b, the output is proportional to ab.

Computers are ideal for data handling and can be programmed to issue a warning if a given measurand exceeds or fails to reach a given level. The warning may take the form of a message on a VDU, a printed message or the automatic sounding of a siren and the shutting down of a whole manufacturing plant. Computers can also save the operator's time by updating the display only when there is a change in the value of the measurand.

Computers are logical machines; they can not only record the measurements but inform the operator what to do about them. Decisions, warnings, advice, predictions and the like are all within the competence of a computer so paving the way to the most sophisticated of measurement systems.

We have said little about display devices, since these are more in the realm of electrical engineering than in electronics. Voltmeters (both moving-coil and digital), printers, plotters, and multi-channel strip-chart recorders are but a few of the vast range of display devices, but we do not have space to describe them here.

Control Systems

The simplest form of control system consists of a measurement system together with a human operator. For example, the temperature of a room can be controlled by having a person to turn on the heater when the room becomes too cold and to turn the heater off when it warms up again. This is what is known as an open loop system (Fig. 10.5). It is a

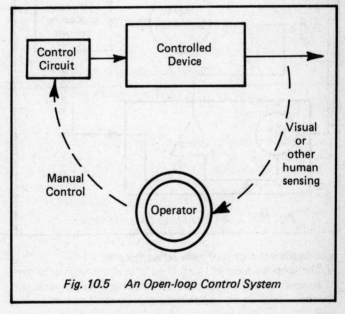

Fig. 10.5   An Open-loop Control System

loop because the operator either watches a thermometer or relies on heat-sensing nerves in the skin and thus knows when the room is too hot or too cold. There is sensory feedback of information from the controlled device (heater) to the operator, who then adjusts the control circuit (heater switch). The feedback is *negative* because the action of the operator is to oppose any change in the room temperature. Negative feedback

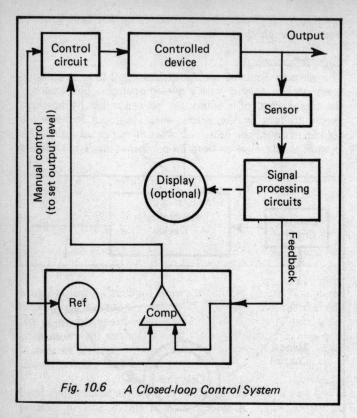

Fig. 10.6   A Closed-loop Control System

is an important aspect of most stable systems.

The loop we have just described is an *open loop* since part of it involves an operator. If the operator is not present the system breaks down and the room becomes too hot or too cold.

Automatic control does away with the need for a human operator by closing the loop with a mechanical or electronic system. A *closed loop* system has a complete mechanical or electronic connection between the sensor and the control circuit (Fig. 10.6). As in a measurement system, the sensor usually needs a processing circuit of one or more stages; these take the form of those already described in the previous

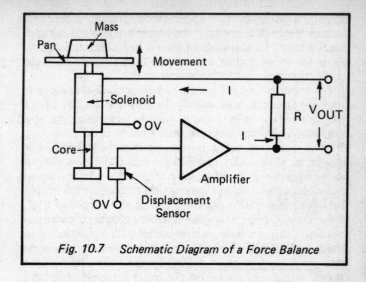

Fig. 10.7   Schematic Diagram of a Force Balance

section. Whether or not the system requires a display to show
the current value of the controlled measurand depends on
what sort of system it is. The essential requirement is that
the loop is completed with circuits that use the information
from the signal processing to control the system. It is also
essential that the system is designed so that the feedback is
negative.

As an example of this, consider the force balance illustrated
in Figure 10.7. A system such as this is able to measure
weights up to about 100kg with an accuracy of about ±0.05%.
The controlling action of the circuit is to hold the core stationary, partly in and partly out of the solenoid, no matter what
force (within reason) is pressing it down. Excess downward
force due to a mass on the scale-pan has to be countered with
additional upward magnetic force. This is obtained by automatically increasing the current I through the coil. The
controlled device is the core and scale-pan. Its position is
monitored by a position sensor, the output V_o of which is
processed by one or more amplifiers to produce the energising
current. The amplifier is wired so that feedback is negative,
i.e. as the core moves down under increased weight, the amount

167

of current increases to oppose the downward movement. Because feedback is negative, the system is stable and the core comes to rest. The amount of current and hence the voltage across the series resistor is a measure of the downward force on the core.

The above is a simple control system in which the feedback from the sensor is used directly to drive the control circuit (the solenoid). Other control systems may make use of a *comparator*. In such a system the output from the processing circuit is compared with a reference voltage. The comparator may be an IC specially designed for that purpose, or we can use an operational amplifier as in Figure 8.9. In the circuit shown there the amplifier is being used to compare the output from the bridge with a reference voltage at the wiper of VR2. If the output drops below the reference voltage, the alarm is sounded. This is a measurement circuit with a comparator to detect a point value of the bridge output. However, the same principle is used in many control systems, the action of the control circuit depending on the input it receives from the comparator.

Although the aim of a control system is to hold a given measurand steady, it is often of practical importance that a certain amount of leeway should be allowed. For example, consider the system of Project 11, intended to keep a constant level of water in a tank. As explained on page 154, it is not satisfactory to have the pump switching on every time a few millilitres of water have been drawn from the tank and switching off a moment later when the tank is refilled by an equivalent small amount. Worse still is the situation in which the circuit is in a half-on/half-off state with the sensor *just* turning on the relay, which chatters on and off in an ineffective fashion. To obtain a more definite action we use two probes at different levels, giving the system a *dead band*. This can also be obtained by using a Schmitt trigger. Figure 10.8 shows a Schmitt trigger based on a non-inverting buffer logic gate. By suitable choice of resistors, the gate can be made to switch on when a *rising* input voltage reaches, say, 5.5V. The output goes high, pulling up (through R2) the voltage at the input. Now V_{IN} has to fall to, say, 4.5V to turn the buffer off and make its output go low.

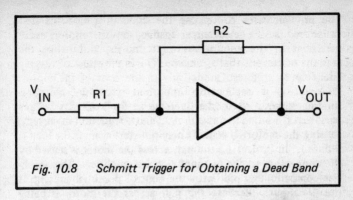

Fig. 10.8   Schmitt Trigger for Obtaining a Dead Band

The main disadvantage of the dead band is that it results in marked fluctuations in the level of the measurand. This may not be acceptable. There is also the problem of *overshoot*, caused by the inertia of the system. For example, a heater needs to be large enough to be able to maintain a room at a fixed temperature. Yet a large heater takes some time to cool down after it has been switched off by the control circuit. This means that it continues heating the room *after* it has been switched off. Conversely once it has been switched off and cooled along with the room, its elements take appreciable time to warm up again *after* it has been switched on. This adds to any fluctuations produced by the dead band. The same effect occurs in speed control systems with the physical inertia of the moving parts. For finer control of levels, some systems use *proportional control*. In this, the output of the system is proportional to the difference between the level detected by the sensor and the reference level. Taking a thermostat room heater as an example, if the room is much colder than it is supposed to be, the heater is switched on at full power. As the temperature approaches the required level, the heater is switched to a lower power rating and the room is heated more slowly to bring it to the final level.

The speed control circuit of Project 12 (following) is perhaps the simplest example of a control system. The speed of a motor varies according to the current supplied to it. The amount of current passing through TR9 to the motor is determined by the output voltage of the operational amplifier.

The problem with controlling the speed of a motor is that variations in the mechanical loading on the motor cause variations in the p.d. across its terminals, and hence the amount of current that is drawn. This is the effect of varying back e.m.f. produced inductively in the coils of the motor. Back e.m.f. is particularly important when the motor is running slowly. A sudden increase in the load may reduce back e.m.f. leading to a rise in p.d., and a reduction in current, causing the motor to stall. It may not start again if the load is reduced. In Project 12 the p.d. across the motor is sensed by the connection to the (−) input of the amplifier. The amplifier compares this p.d. with the control potential present at the (+) input. Because the p.d. across the motor is being sensed by the (−) input, the system has negative feedback. An increase of p.d. results in a fall in the output of the amplifier and hence a reduction of the current through TR9. The p.d. across the motor is thus restored almost instantly to the same level as that at the (+) input. Thus the system is a closed loop which maintains a steady p.d. across the motor. It runs smoothly under varying loads, even at very low speeds.

PROJECT 12 – Model Speed Controller (Level 3)

This is intended as an automatic speed controller for model railways, though it could also be adapted for controlling the speed of other models powered by an electric motor.

How It Works
The section of the circuit which controls the speed of the motor is on page 174. Its action, described in the section above, allows the motor to run smoothly at all speeds, lending realism to the model. If S1 is switched to VR5, this operates as a manual speed control, which overrides the automatic control. When control is automatic, one of the relays RLA to RLD is switched on, connecting the (+) input of IC6 to one of the variable resistors VR1 to VR4. These are each pre-set to supply a different voltage to the amplifier and thus cause the motor to operate at different predetermined speeds.

The automatic control system on pages 172–173 takes its input from a number of sensors placed at strategic points on the railway layout. The diagram shows 4 sensors, but the design is readily modified for fewer sensors, or for more. The sensors are optical sensors, each consists of a photo-transistor (TR1 to TR4) and a pull-up resistor (R3 to R6). Normally the phototransistor is illuminated by room lighting or daylight and the voltage at its collector is low. When the transistor is shaded by a passing locomotive the output of the sensor rises briefly, to a high logic levels.

The logic of the system is designed to switch on the relay corresponding to the sensor most recently passed by the train. For example, two sensors might be situated at the beginning and end of a particularly tortuous section of the track. As the train enters this portion, it passes the first sensor and its speed is automatically reduced. As it leaves this portion it passes the second sensor and its speed is increased again.

The J–K flip-flops of IC4 and IC5 act as memory units, one for each sensor. J–K flip-flops change their state only when they are triggered by pulses from a clock. The clock (IC1) runs at about 70Hz and any of the flip-flops may change state as the clock output rises from low to high. Whether a flip-flop changes or not depends on the state of its J and K inputs:

	J	K	Out Q change
1	Low	Low	No change
2	High	Low	Goes high
3	Low	High	Goes low
4	High	High	Changes to opposite

$\overline{Q}$ is always the opposite of Q. Each time a sensor is passed, the corresponding memory unit is set (Q high) and the other three are reset (Q low). The J inputs are normally high and, in a flip-flop that is reset, the $\overline{Q}$ output and K input are high. When a sensor is passed, the low level at the J input makes the flip-flop change state; its Q output goes from low to high (transition 3 above). At the same time the high pulse from the sensor goes to the OR gates controlling the other three

171

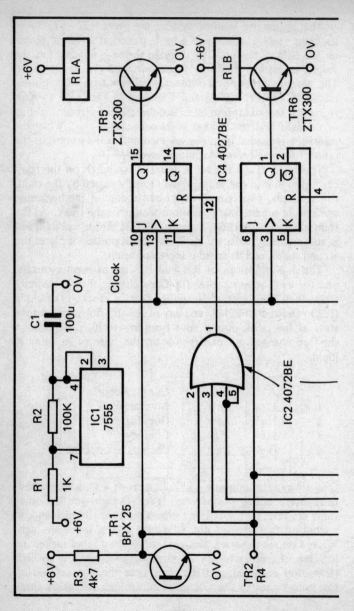

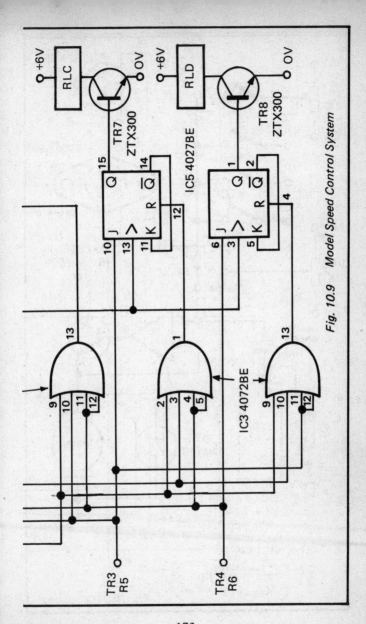

Fig. 10.9   Model Speed Control System

173

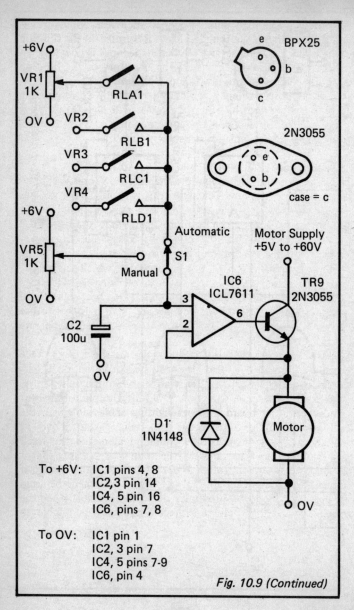

Fig. 10.9 (Continued)

174

flip-flops. The high pulses passes to their reset inputs, resetting them; their Q outputs go low. Returning to the flip-flop which has just been set, we see that its K input is now low. In this state (transitions 1 and 2) the Q output of the flip-flop can not change back to low except by resetting it.

In summary, when a sensor is passed, the corresponding flip-flop is set and the others are reset. The high Q output of the set flip-flop energises the corresponding relay, so connecting *one* of the variable resistors to the amplifier.

Construction

The sensors and logic require a stabilised 5V or 6V supply. The total power requirement for this is about 20mA, so it is feasible to use a 6V battery. The supply required by the motor may be considerably more than this. As Figure 10.9 shows, the motor can be driven by a separate DC power supply, possibly the power pack normally used to operate the railway system. TR9 is a power transistor, which can pass up to 15A, at a voltage of up to 60V. When used with high current or voltage it should be mounted on a heat sink. Since the currents switched by the relays are small it is best to use sub-miniature or ultra-miniature PCB relays rated to operate on 5V or 6V.

There are several ways of implementing the sensors. One simple technique suited to a railway system set out on a baseboard is to bore a hole in the board between the rails, so that the train passes over the hole. Mount the phototransistor underneath the board. Room lighting shines down on the phototransistor except when the train passes above it. Alternatively, sensors can be mounted alongside the track so that they are shaded when the train passes. Note that it is possible to employ other types of sensor in this system if desired, provided that they give a low pulse when the train is detected; the metal proximity detector of Project 6 and the sound operated switch of Project 8 are both adaptable to this system.

Details of Special Parts

Semiconductors

D1   1N4148 silicon signal diode
TR1–TR4   BPX25 silicon phototransistor
TR5–TR8   ZTX300 npn transistor
TR9   2N3055 npn power transistor

Integrated Circuits

IC1   7555 CMOS timer
IC2, IC3   4072BE CMOS dual 4-input OR gate
IC4, IC5   4027BE CMOS dual J–K flip-flop
IC6   ICL7611 CMOS operational amplifier

Appendix

Integrated Circuits
Figure A.1 shows the connections for CMOS integrated circuits which have four 2-pin gates, the 4001, 4011, 4070, and for the 4050 hex buffer IC.

Construction for Beginners
The following books will help the beginner who lacks experience of construction techniques:

227	Beginners Guide to Building Electronic Projects
BP7	Radio Electronic Colour Codes Data Chart
BP48	Electronic Projects for Beginners
BP110	How to Get Your Electronic Projects Working
BP121	How to Design and Make Your Own PCB's
BP127	How to Design Electronic Projects
BP239	Getting the Most From Your Multimeter

Suppliers
Pyroelectric sensors and other components are available from: Electromail, PO Box 33, Corby, Northants NN17 9EL. Telephone: (0536) 204555.

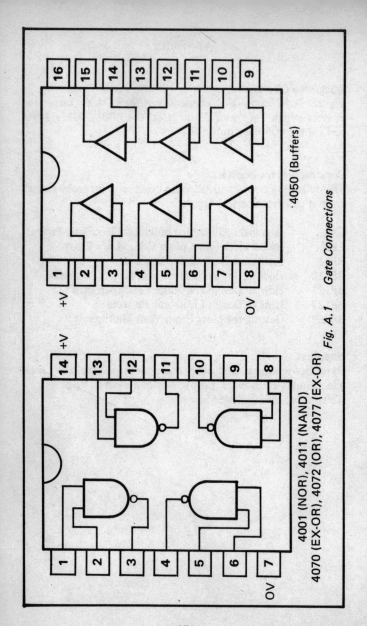

4050 (Buffers)

4001 (NOR), 4011 (NAND)
4070 (EX-OR), 4072 (OR), 4077 (EX-OR)

Fig. A.1   Gate Connections

178